MAYHEM
IN
FRANCE

Cy Charles Ross

Copyright: CyCharlesRoss©2016

Author: Cy Charles Ross

First Published: May 2016 CreateSpace

Second Edition Published: September 2016

Published by: Independent Publishing Network

Printed by: Imprint Digital September 2016

ISBN: 978-1-78280-921-0

DEDICATION

I would like to dedicate this book to Ursula, in recognition of the love and laughter we have shared during the last 27 years, and for her support whilst writing this book.

ACKNOWLEDGEMENTS

My grateful thanks goes to Lesley Bond, Hazel Tamkin, Betty Quinnel and Siobhan Worthington-Lavery my agent, for their invaluable help with the editing and production of this book.

CHAPTER 1

The year was 1943, and it was only a few months ago that I had joined the Armed Forces. A young man, barely into adulthood. Since then, events had happened so quickly; I was now flying over the English Channel.

Glancing downward, I saw that the English Channel was no longer there and realised I must now be flying over occupied France. Enemy territory! I became scared. I'd felt so good and brave when volunteering, but now reality had joined the equation. Questions and doubts emerged. 'How proficient was my pilot flying at tree top level in moonlight?' It was only a small single-engine plane. 'What if we crashed, or our destination was occupied by a German reception committee instead of members of the French resistance?' I tried not to think of what would happen to me, should I be captured, not being in uniform. I was very apprehensive. In desperation, I focussed my mind. 'How had it all developed to this stage?'

On joining up, I had made a preference to join the Royal Marines and thought that I had all the credentials to do so. The three years, since I was seventeen, I had spent in the Home Guard had been so beneficial, especially so the weaponry. Also, there were drills, parades, assault courses, patrol skills and manoeuvers with regular Army personnel. During air raids, I had done bicycle patrols with a rifle across my back - looking out for German paratroopers - and shot down German bomber crews. There had also been railway bridges and other strategic sites to mount an Armed Guard. So yes, I was extremely confident; a full blooded Aries, capable of anything and knew everything. (A notorious youthful characteristic.) Thus, I was completely shattered when the military establishment decided instead to draft me into the Fleet Air Arm - a specialised branch of the Royal Navy - instead of the Royal Marines; presumably because of my previous employment in telecommunications and allied electrical work. I was to be employed in the electrical maintenance of aircraft.

It was a big disappointment to me. Almost all of the enthusiastic youth of the day wished to enrol in their own ideal service at the outbreak of war, but it was not to be for me.

After a course on basic aircraft electrics and weapon instruction, plus vigorous assault courses and disciplinary naval procedures, I was posted to a Royal Naval Air Station to gain experience of aircraft maintenance. The airfield was in progress of being built. All the buildings were complete, likewise the runway, and it should soon be operational. The Fleet Air Arm, being in its infancy, was in the process of expanding so that, initially, the Fleet Air Arm personnel were in the minority; the bases being mainly staffed by the R.A.F.

To speed up the construction, a few of us were diverted from aircraft maintenance to cable and communication work. At first, a Flight Sergeant was in charge; the work coming to an abrupt halt when he went sick and the stores ran out of cable clips. During the halt in the construction, I managed to have a look at the Flight Sergeant's diagrams. I could not believe that such a vast amount of cable was being used. I was sure I could make modifications that would save cable and time.

After a couple of days of non-productive work, a Flight Lieutenant arrived on the scene, having been sent to ascertain the stoppage. I told him the reason being a shortage of cable clips. I suggested that workshops could quite easily stamp out thousands of them, with their machines, from waste aircraft metal. I also mentioned the cable excess. It was obvious that it wasn't in his line at all. He was not interested. He was probably in admin, or in another section, and had just been detailed to explain the delay.

He looked at me, paused, slightly frowned and said, "It will all have to go to the Wing Commander for him to see and decide." Another pause, then he continued, "I will pass this to the Wing Commander, including this cable business. His word is law around here. The Wing Commander will sort it out and you too. I think you are just a young upstart!"

I answered that statement but made sure he didn't hear it.

Later, the Flight Lieutenant came for me and took me to see the Wing Commander. I had not seen him before. I expected to see a reasonably young character, because all the R.A.F. personnel seemed to be so. Not so this Wing Commander. I suppose that his flying days were over and he was now in admin, using his vast experience.

He peered at me from under his eyebrows, glasses on the end of his nose, prepared to give me a few minutes of his valuable time. After I had given him the details, and an idea of the sizes of clips to be manufactured by workshops, and a possible saving of cable and time, he stopped his hurry up attitude. I assured him that I could calculate the different sizes and their quantity if the modifications were worked out, and the different size cables were known. He then asked me about my civilian employment.

After I had given him a brief description, he was lost in thought for a few moments, then "Alright!" he stated, "I will give you this small anteroom, adjacent to my office. I will give you a chit to order anything you need for your drawings to collect from stores. You will have to come through my office, but I don't want any disturbance. No saluting, no knocking at the door. If you see a no entry sign on my door, you will not enter. Otherwise, come and go as you please. When completed, submit it to me. Now get on with it!"

Sometime later, when I had completed it, I submitted it to him and, after studying it, he seemed quite impressed. He said,

"It will have to be scrutinised by others before a decision is taken to implement it, and even then there might be modifications."

A few days later, we received permission to proceed with the installation.

It was maybe a fortnight later that I was suddenly ordered to the Wing Commander's office. I wondered why, and was not sure whether to be concerned or not. 'Had I dropped a clanger with my drawings? What other reason could there be to warrant this abrupt order?' I became more concerned after each step, on my way to the Wing Commander's office.

The Flight Lieutenant and I duly appeared at the office door. He knocked, then showed me into the office and, quietly closing the door, went on his way.

I mentioned earlier that I was concerned, but nothing as concerned as when I entered the room and saw such an array of people in front of me! Even more so, when I saw the Group Captain with the Wing Commander and two gentlemen in suits, all seated behind a table. I felt overawed and apprehensive, yet even so, I smiled to myself and felt inwardly amused that all of them were trying to find enough room for their knees to fit under the average sized table. This amusement lurched to the suited gentlemen, who added a sinister ingredient to the mix.

I quickly took stock of them. One was middle aged; slightly plump; with a chubby face and receding hair; with more hair at both sides of his head, but actually bald on top. He was dressed in a dark grey suit with a waistcoat. The other gentleman was younger; in his early thirties; dark hair, short back and sides; lantern jawed, a man's man. He had a face with intent and wore a dark blue suit.

I had a sudden glimmer of hope when I detected a slight, reassuring smile from the Wing Commander. All those

8

observations and inner feelings took place in the few moments on entering the room.

'Groupy' looked up at me and requested, "Sit down, we wish you to relax whilst we ask you a few questions." After a pause, and showing a very concerned and serious face he continued, "Have you always been circuitry minded?"

I replied, "Yes Sir, I have a great desire to draw and design circuits in my spare time." I was aware that 'Blue Suit' and 'Baldy' were intently analysing and taking stock of me as I spoke.

"Would you rather have stayed at home in your civilian job to carry on doing just that?" he continued.

"No, I was eager to join up like others in my own age group."

"Why?" asked 'Baldy' suddenly.

I turned my head to look at him and confidently replied, "To help defend my country. That is why I joined the Home Guard at 17."

"You must love your country then?" said 'Baldy'.

I thought that was a stupid question, but I managed to say, with head held high, "Of course I do, I think everybody loves their country and would naturally defend it."

I was beginning to feel annoyed and cocky. I was naturally a self-confident person. Then yet another irritating question. 'Blue Suit' asked, "Would you be prepared to risk your life doing just that?"

"We are all expected to do that by joining the Armed Forces." I replied.

He slowly nodded his head, and faintly smiled, questioning more intensely "Yes, that is so. I shall put it to you another way. Would you consider doing a vitally important job, which would involve going into occupied territory?"

I was somewhat taken aback. 'What possible job could I do and where would it be?'

"Would you consider it or would it be too daunting for you?" asked 'Baldy', shooting me a sideways look.

Confused, I stammered, "It's just so sudden a question and I don't know what would be expected of me."

"Oh, no fighting or physical violence, nothing like that, just helping us by using the expertise which you appear to have."

I was now beginning to feel positive inside. Something important to do for my country. Other lads of my age would love such an opportunity. I turned to face them confidently. "If you think I could cope with it, whatever it is, then the answer is yes."

'Groupy' suddenly broke in. "Think about it and report back to Wing Commander in two days."

"I've already thought about it Sir."

'Baldy' and 'Blue Suit' smiled wryly.

"No!" said 'Groupy', very sternly, "I said in two days' time!"

I was then dismissed, albeit for them to have detailed discussions about me. I could do nothing else but think about the meeting.

My mind raced; 'Where could it be? No fighting? No physical violence? What kind of war will I be in? Sounds like an office job with diagrams, maybe in an embassy somewhere. That's not what I joined up for, and another thing, occupied territory!' I was puzzled and intrigued for the next two days.

I duly reported to the Wing Commander two days later. He did not have any more details, but he came over all fatherly and explained, "You don't have to do this. You can always reverse the decision at any time. Remember that and back out of it."

It wasn't very long before I was ushered into an adjoining office to the Wing Commander's. Once again 'Baldy' and 'Blue Suit' were there. They didn't seem as stiff and formal as on the first occasion. "No doubt you want to know what this is all about don't you?" said 'Baldy'.

I replied, "Yes, I do, very much so. Where will I be going and for how long? What will be required of me?"

"Whoa, Whoa, Whoa! Not so fast" said 'Blue Suit' cutting in with a grin.

Wing Commander suddenly interrupted. "I will leave you now to carry on your interview gentlemen." With a hint of a smile in my direction, he left the room.

A silence ensued, whilst the Wing commander departed, then 'Baldy' resumed, "It may be that you will be exposed to a certain amount of danger from enemy forces whilst you are abroad, but we will educate you to minimise it. You will not be involved in any fighting. We don't expect you to be. We cannot give you any details about your mission, because of security, but it will be allied to your knowledge of telecommunications."

'Blue Suit' added, "We want to send you over to France as soon as possible. Regarding your fitness, you have done your share of assault courses, so there will be no need to do any more of them. You will carry out preparatory procedures and training, including a parachute landing course. (I thought 'Wow!') You must familiarise yourself with German uniforms. Get used to them, so that you will not be daunted if indeed you become close to them."

"What about the language difficulty?" I asked. "I do know a certain amount of French, learnt at school."

"Fatal!" said 'Baldy' butting in. "You will only use the phrases taught by us, unless of course you are only amongst French friends. Otherwise your pigeon English/French would soon give you away. We will teach you some German, but I can't envisage you having much in the way of conversation.

"You will sign the Secrets Act and, once signed, you must strictly abide by it throughout your life. If you cannot continue at any time, or become sick with fear of what might happen to you; I must stress to you that we understand that it can happen, and it has, many times. You may withdraw from the operation at any time before embarkation. I repeat, at any time. There will be no shame attached whatsoever and the whole of your period with us will be erased from your records. You must go on a diet, although you tend to have a thin face and be the greyhound type. You look far too healthy to be an East European."

"East European?" I questioned.

"Yes" replied 'Lantern jaw', grinning. "Don't concern yourself about that aspect, it will all fall into place. Another thing, we will have to stop you smiling so much, and you must droop your shoulders a little. I know you don't actually smile excessively, but it is also in your eyes. We will have to put a stop to that. Your glasses are universal, made in Germany by Zeiss so they are not a problem."

And with that, we were done.

CHAPTER 2

About two weeks later I started my training; learning and digesting basics. Don't look right when you cross the road; a real give away. Always act the part.

"If you have a disguise. Which I don't think will apply." said the instructor. "Be realistic. If you have to limp, don't forget to, and remember which limb it is by putting something in your shoe to make you limp."

I had lessons in unarmed combat: How to fight in a knife fight; how to keep your opponent guessing as to whether you were left handed or right handed; how to kill from different angles. In a front attack, thrust the knife upwards under the ribs into the heart, thereby missing the hard rib cage protection. Yes, there were more ghastly details and methods, not very pretty, but essential when a young man is fighting a war and learning all the possible ways to stay alive. These days I go out of my way to avoid treading on any creepy crawly!

I assembled and reassembled Sten guns in a class and was quickest at it, courtesy of my time in the Home Guard.

I once said to the instructor, "Why all this training? I thought there wasn't to be any violence!" Others asked the same question and received the same answer. "Better to be prepared just in case."

Whilst I was there, it was the practise to ask any question via the female Secretary; a forbidding, middle-aged woman, yet very polite and understanding when listening to one's question. The system was that she would convey the question to the expert in that field, but most of the time she knew the answers to the questions. She hardly smiled, was strict on procedure and seemed to be held in high esteem by the authorities.

After finishing my tuition, I was posted to Woodford in Cheshire to join a mass of military personnel learning how to drop and land from a Gantry.

There were quite a few Polish Army types training there, learning this fine art. They were great characters. The R.A.F. boys seemed to get on well with the 'Polskies', who were so intent on learning English.

I remember one-day travelling on a bus from Benchill to Manchester, when I witnessed the comedic result of the R.A.F. Polish association. The bus was quite full and I was seated near the rear of the bus, when a Polish Army soldier stood up from his seat and, like a true polite gentleman - which Polish men seemed to be - offered his seat to a middle aged lady with the words. "Please put your arse down here madam!"

My happiness being at Woodford was short lived when I received orders to return. I was very disappointed because there was so much camaraderie and I hadn't even had a drop!

On returning, I was told there was a change of plan; I would not now be parachuting in. I heard that a number of reasons had resulted in this decision; a big risk of injury on landing and being dropped off target, (the plane could be plotted on radar and therefore be a target). I was to go by Lysander, a small single engine aircraft, which I was told could take off and land in 300 yards and could fly underneath the radar, so it would be a hedge hopping job which would mean going only on a clear night.

At first I was disappointed. I had been looking forward to the instruction at Woodford. There was such a lot of great humour and comradeship, especially with the 'Polskies'.

When I returned, I was fitted out with clothes quite quickly, but there was a big delay on footwear. I never knew why. I know that there was a lot of concern about it. I didn't think it was my size 11's that was the problem. Perhaps East Europeans have little feet?

Awaiting the final phase, my advisor told me that the Lysander (Lizzie) now had a black metal ladder fitted to the port side to speed up entry and exit. All the hanging about was making me jittery. I told my advisor about it. We were supposed to report our feelings. I said that sometimes I got 'cold feet' and a little apprehensive.

He said, "Don't worry about it, it's normal, even for the experts. If you find you can't sleep, start sweating about it, or find it is taking over your whole being, you must tell me or Miss Secretary."

CHAPTER 3

Eventually, the evening arrived for me to prepare to leave for the airstrip. I was surprised to see the Secretary there. She came to me before I went through the door to the awaiting car. She hugged me and whispered, "God keep you safe." There were tears in her eyes.

On the way to the airfield I felt like a bag of nerves. The briefing chief said, "Don't worry son, the pilot has done this before. He's not a rookie like you."

At the airfield, there was no celebrity departure, no good luck voices. The pilot was on board and we just went quickly up. I had not flown before, neither had the population at large, so it was an added load of nerves in the bag. After a while into the flight I looked down and, even though it was moonlight, I couldn't see much below and I didn't especially wish to do so. Everything seemed to be whizzing past and I was all jammed in with lots of merchandise in sacks. I didn't know our destination.

Sometime, through downward glances, I saw the English Channel finish and knew then that we were over occupied territory. Enemy territory! It was then that it really hit me. I suddenly felt scared to death. Once again my mind raced. 'How far have we got to go? Where? I've inflicted this situation on myself! It was so great and patriotic in the Wing Commander's office, a lot different in reality. Fancy volunteering for this certain death you stupid sod! Lizzie has only one engine, what if we were to crash land? It doesn't bear thinking about. What if our destination has a German reception committee?' I was almost sick with fright and the terrible tension I had developed. I tried not to think of what awaited me.

I was acting and thinking like a real 'Nancy'. 'Take a grip of yourself. Just pack it in!' After giving myself a severe telling off, I started to relax.

To relieve the tension, I started comparing my present situation with the other choice. I'd heard that the draft I had been with at the airbase were about to be posted to the Pacific, on an aircraft carrier, to fight the Japanese; an alternative to being on Lizzie. I would be just as vulnerable. I could be torpedoed, bombed, burnt or eaten by a shark! Not a lot of choice but I would not have been on my own. Yet again, I started up thoughts. 'This plane is so light and so small that if we came up against a headwind we would end up stationary.' This stupid childlike humour helped me a bit. I would normally be fast asleep at this time.

Then the plane started circling. I thought, 'Oh God, we must be here!' We were weaving from side to side. I think the pilot was trying to get a better view of the ground because the plane had a good forward vision. I peered down but just could not absorb it, everything was rushing past so very fast, yet the pilot must have been able to see far afield. Then suddenly we stabilized. Perhaps the ground lights had only just been switched on, because we were going straight in. Suddenly we were down, touching down beautifully in the dark and coming very quickly to a halt.

I almost leapt down the ladder to the ground and, as I landed on the terra firma, I'm certain I heard the pilot shout "You must be mad!" Of course we had not been able to communicate on the journey because there was a long length of fuselage between us, housing the main fuel tank. I would have been far from deliriously happy if I had known that on my journey.

I glanced back and saw a few men man-handling the merchandise from the aircraft. I noticed that the pilot remained firmly in his seat. I hardly had time to gather my thoughts before Lizzie took off in the flicker of an eye and was gone.

Two men grabbed me by the arms saying, "Bonsoir Monsieur." Then hustled me into a Saloon car.

The driver was in the car, which was ticking over, yet I could not believe the noise that was coming from the men handling the freight and transferring it into another vehicle. They were talking loudly, with the odd 'guffaw'. Not what I had been expecting. It had been impressed upon me to maintain the utmost silence and speed when disembarking. It could surely put us all in danger?

Not so my companions, they were very quiet, moving swiftly into the car. One slid in next to the driver, the other shared the rear seat with me, sitting on my left. He offered me a cigarette, which I really appreciated and accepted with a trembling hand. I was about to start a conversation, but he gave me a friendly smile and put his finger to his lips. No one spoke as we sped off into the darkness.

We had been travelling for about twenty minutes, when the front passenger grunted as we slowed down, approaching a check point. My companion slid his arm, I presume, into a shoulder holster and withdrew it complete with handgun.

"Why the hell have I not got a gun to defend myself?" I hissed.

He again gave me the finger on lips sign and grinned; probably to put me at ease. It did, but only a little bit.

We came to a halt. I felt extremely tense. Rapid French ensued on both sides, then "Merci." from the front man as we sped off. It was only then that my companion homed his gun, sat back and relaxed into his seat.

We had been travelling a long time when suddenly we stopped again at another check point. Once again my blood pressure went up to maximum as we had the same procedure with the handgun, but this time a gendarme put his head through the front passenger window to look at me and said, "Bonsoir Monsieur."

My companion had his gun immediately levelled at his head, but first the front man laughed, then the driver, and lastly the companion, whilst lowering his gun. I could also hear laughter from the check point staff as we moved away to resume our journey. I was beginning to feel that this was a funny dream; this wasn't supposed to happen. I had been feeling tired, what with the adrenaline flow and the apprehension of not knowing what was to come. Yet, although weary, I felt somehow wide awake, ready for the unexpected. I was trying to comprehend our check point stops, when suddenly the car pulled up outside the entrance to what appeared to be a large barn.

The four of us got out of the car. One of my companions stayed by the car, the other two led me inside. I glimpsed what looked like a toilet on the left hand side, just inside the door. I followed the other two through straw and passed wheatsheaves. I could see and feel the concentrated stares from what looked like a few farm labourers. 'God!' I thought, 'they must start work early.'

At the far end of the barn, we stepped up on to another level and entered into a small alcove on the right hand side. The barn resembled an inverted letter L and was quite deep in straw.

My companions indicated that this was the end of the journey and that I was to stay in the alcove. One of my companions disappeared, then returned with some cheese, croissants and coffee. They hugged me and kissed me on both cheeks then, smiling, left me to eat and drink. I thought, at the time, that I did not like this hugging and kissing between blokes. I would risk a punch in the nose if I ever tried it back home!

There was no communication from the labourers who were talking loudly and gesticulating. It was too far away to hear what the commotion was about. I felt like a nervous wreck after my dreadful long tense journey, not knowing where the hell I was. Not being in charge of my own destiny and feeling very tired had a lot to do with it.

After a very nervous hour, a small, slim looking woman arrived. I guessed that she would be in her early thirties, dressed in a knee length warm looking skirt with bits of straw attached. A very heavy looking material covered her top half, with a velvet beret on her head. Seeing me, she smiled. "Ah! Anglais?" I nodded, then she broke into almost perfect English, "Welcome to this dreadful hole!"

I said "God, you speak English. I haven't had a conversation since leaving England."

She was smiling and, looking very sympathetic, said, "I'll introduce myself. We all have code names here, then, if we are caught and interrogated it can't do any damage. I have been advised to call you Oliver, and I am Olive to you. How do you do?!" with her hand held out in a mocking English way of introduction. Then, stepping forward, kissed me on both cheeks. "Mon brave Anglais." she said.

I was beginning to 'thaw out' and feel a bit calmer now with this woman oozing confidence and friendship. I was about to ask her who advised her regarding the names, but she prattled on, "We two have something in common."

"Oh?" I said with raised eyebrows.

"Yes we have. All the others here are 'Frenchies'. I am from the Pyrenees area between France and Spain," and then, very surprised on my part, she said "I am so glad you have come to join us. You are not welcomed by the others. They don't want some naïve Anglais being dropped in amongst them. They would have much preferred more merchandise, the same as

20

came with you on the plane. Of course, they don't know what you are here for do they?"

I thought, 'they are not the only ones, neither do I!'

She carried on saying, "They only see what is just in front of them, not the broader strategy of the war, being French." She stopped for a moment then said, "They don't need an escape hatch. Most of them can go home."

I said, "Escape hatch? Where?"

"Here, at the end, covered up, but plenty big enough to crawl through, and you can pull up the straw behind you. Hopefully you won't need it."

Suddenly, "You don't mind bedding down with me do you? Fully clothed" she said, with a grin. "You're not funny or anything?" she teased.

"No, I'm damn well not!"

"Just checking," she said with an amused expression. "Only, it gets damn cold during the night at this time of the year." A pause, then, "I know that you must be on edge not knowing anything and in strange surroundings, but someone will come and give you instructions and advice tomorrow." Then she smiled and said, "Don't worry, I will look after you."

Later, she took me down to the entrance to the barn and showed me the very rough toilet, containing buckets and a tap and metal tank with a ballcock valve on it. "You won't be on the rota to empty it Oliver and neither will I. You can also wash in cold water. A proper clean job and shave can be done at one or other of the member's houses, but not as often as you would like. Don't worry, you get used to all the B.O. eventually." she laughed.

We went back to our corner and, as the light faded, she lit a wicker lamp in the alcove. It wasn't visible from the barn door. "It's getting chilly now so we'll tuck down if you wish. You must be completely whacked out."

I admitted it.

We laid down in our clothes next to each other and talked a little. She said "I live in a lovely mountain village and my mother is part English and part Spanish. She is a school teacher and would love to live in England one day."

"What, for God's sake, made you decide to come here?" I questioned.

"Well, Mother and I both think and speak English and are helping the best, and probably the only way, we can."

"Where's your Mother now?"

"Don't ask Oliver, just don't ask!"

"Do you go out with other members?"

"Oh, no never, I'm a courier, but mostly I'm based here."

I don't remember going to sleep, but I awoke during the night lying on my right side. Suddenly I was wide awake. 'God, it's true! It's not a ghastly dream. My God it is true! I can feel the straw to prove it, and Olive tucked into my back with her arms wrapped around me in a vice like grip.' I suppose I was a supercharged hot water bottle to her, because I do give off a tremendous amount of heat when in bed, and Olive seemed to be taking full advantage of it. 'Wow, it is real life, definitely not a dream!' I started thinking. (Not a good idea in the middle of the night; trying to work things out, unless it is positive thinking or planning.) I came to the conclusion that I would not survive.

So much was stacked against me. Any odd little mishap: an expression, betrayal, a false move, and then I would be a goner. I didn't even know where I was, nor did I know why and what I would be doing! I sincerely hoped it would not be with this antagonistic mob. 'What about the aftermath of capture? The interrogation? Torture, then shot!' I was a real miserable sod during the early hours, far from being a happy bunny.

I must have dropped off to sleep. I awoke because Olive was extracting herself from me. I looked at her and grimly smiled. Her face lit up and she said. "It's been the warmest night yet. You can definitely stay!" and off she went, looking over her shoulder smiling and saying, "I'm getting breakfast."

Her attitude, full of normality, positive and so friendly, washed away most of the overnight pessimistic attitude. 'Olive has survived hasn't she? Well so can I! Stop being so damn fretful. Go for it, because you have just got to.'

Olive came back with a bagful of croissants and a jug of coffee. Chatting over our breakfast she told me that she could speak fluent French, Spanish and English. A mock questioning and anxious expression enveloped her face as she said "English", which made me laugh and I said, "Yes Olive, I can just about understand your English." That remark earned me some straw in my breakfast.

I told her about my family and the British style of living in the present wartime Britain. Also, about the lovely countryside in the spring; the near misses I had had during the bombing and whilst serving in the Home Guard. She told me about her near misses; near targets being bombed by allied planes.

Suddenly, she said, "I can't ever see me having children, my mother nearly died having me; I was a breech birth. That is why I just have a very close girlfriend, it's much safer."

All these personal confidences with each other would not happen in normal life. I had noticed it before, people were closer in wartime and formed a common bond in the face of danger, living for each day and so seemingly imperative to confide very personal matters. We chatted, getting on tremendously well. Two kindred souls I suppose.

Suddenly we had a visitor. As soon as he appeared, Olive smiled. He came over to me and, after I had extracted myself from the straw, we shook hands. Speaking English, with a slight imperfection, he said his name was Monsieur De Cautemps. That is what it sounded like. He was very calm and polite, and had a vet insignia on his left lapel. "Initially you are here to help tap in to the German telephone network from this region." He let that sink in for a moment, then gave me a map of the area and telephone numbers. He gave me the numbers to be tapped, but not their location. "You must now liaise with Henri and Olive. Henri is here most days. You will have to go out and mingle."

He gave me a forged 'Trusty Pass'. I was not to attempt to speak French and to speak only the German I had practised in England. I was a Latvian trustee.

CHAPTER 4

During the early part of the war, Russia invaded Latvia and Estonia and occupied them. When Hitler declared war on Russia he went through Poland and 'liberated' Latvia and Estonia. As a result, many people volunteered to join the German army. My story was that, unfortunately, as a Latvian, I suffered from fits and was unable to join the German army. I had come to France in a non-combat position, a friend or helper to the German army. Therefore, I had a pass signed by an OBS LT who had since been posted from the area.

Monsieur De Cautemps reminded me. "You must remember to be friendly to German personnel, they are your friends..." he said, "but don't overdo it. Don't show your pass unless it is demanded. Although highly improbable, if you do see or hear of any Latvian or Estonian, avoid them like the plague."

I was given details of precautions to exercise that would help to keep me alive. "Henri will call with more tactical information to form a more comprehensive plan. Olive will be part of the operation. She is very, very street wise and is the main person for you. She knows all the tricks and will keep you safe." Monsieur De Cautemps impressed upon me.

I spent all that day and the next day in the barn. Olive kept disappearing, sometimes for a few hours, but she always came back with a meal of meat or different pastries and bread. The majority of the meals had an infusion of herbs which I had not known before, due to living in isolated Britain, so used to 'unadulterated' food.

Henri came very early one morning. "There's Henri, he's talking very loud to the others. He should be coming over shortly." Olive stated.

A little later he came over to us, stared at me, shook hands and said, "I expected someone older." Smiling as he said so. He was a man in his forties; a lot of sandy hair turning grey, even his face appeared sandy with freckles. He had a woollen mixture coat and thick looking medium brown trousers. A gesticulating person, prone to moving his face and shoulders, as well as his arms.

After the greeting and welcome, Henri stated, "You will come now and meet the others in the group. It is essential." He was a very confident and determined character. I should think he could be quite aggressive.

I was very surprised to find the group so amicable. Olive told me later that Henri had explained my position to the group in a very forceful way. I uttered a few words in French to them, which caused some amusement. One character came over, patted me on the back and laughingly greeted me with, "Merci, Merci!" Some were still standing, eating breakfast, including one big burly, swarthy looking character in a very worn looking attire, who was near me and grinning; seemingly very friendly. He was like some of the others, still having his breakfast. He brought his right hand up to his mouth and crunched his teeth into quite a large onion, just like one eats an apple. I could not believe it and at breakfast too. Yuk!

Henri went away for a while and Olive and I returned to our corner. I mentioned the onion character. "Hmm." She said, laughing. "He comes from Brittany. Don't get too fond of him, he's smelly at both ends. He's very windy!"

Henri returned and we got down to some serious discussions. The location of various friendly receptor telephones was noted. "Regarding tapping procedures, the cross connections, if made at the distribution point, would be restricted to only a few and I would need an information diagram, or diagram of the distribution point locations. It would be much safer to do the cross connection inside the exchange on the Main Distribution Frame." I stated.

Henri went quiet and thought for a minute. "We will get the diagram and information for you, and see if any of our receptors are suitable. I would prefer it to be done outside if possible."

"If I could gain access I would do the circuitry. It would be no problem for me, it is only a simple operation. Otherwise, we will have a restricted number of receptors."

"We will try my way first. Have a look at the information and proceed from there. I would prefer it that way." Henri insisted.

Two days later, Henri returned, informing me, "We have your diagram. It must be picked up tomorrow at 3.30 pm. You must go with Olive; it will be good for you."

"I must have a shave and a good clean up if I am going into town tomorrow." I was beginning to feel quite unclean.

"No, it's not essential. Probably be better to look a bit grubby, you will be less conspicuous, no one will give you a second glance."

I thought 'damn, there goes an opportunity for a lovely good scrub at the farmhouse'. Being meticulous regarding my personal hygiene, I craved for a really good serious hot water soap session.

Next morning, I used the ice cold water as much as I could with the rough carbolic type soap, to try and get a reasonably clean result. I did not endeavour to wash my hair or have a shave. When I came out Olive was laughing, "Was it worth it Oliver? No one will notice after all the 'pain' you have been through. Don't concern yourself so much."

Then came the game plan. Olive began, "We will go into town together. We will enter the café and, once inside, you will bear right into the second seating area, which is one step higher than the seating area near the window. Just act casually and sit anywhere. You don't have to order anything; people often come in and stay a while. I will go upstairs to see my girlfriend.

"For security, someone rings the café from the property, (holding the diagram) twice a day." Olive continued. "No one speaks. The telephone is not answered. The Germans are known to raid a property and then wait for contacts to visit and fall into the trap. If no reassuring telephone rings are received, we must, on no account, venture anywhere near the property. It is then essential to raise the unsafe property alarm."

The time came and we commenced the long walk into town. Although I was, to put it mildly, very tense, I was also somewhat concerned as to what I was about to face and how I would cope. The only redeeming feature was the exercise, which I felt was doing me a world of good.

As we approached the town, Olive gave me the last instructions, "If we are separated, you will come out of the café, then turn left in the square, then left again until you arrive at a dark green house door, approximately 75 metres on the left. Don't stand and knock, just open the door and walk in, closing the door behind you."

We eventually reached the café and, opening the door, walked into an open room. There was a small open room on the right, with a window which looked out on to the street. Olive walked on alongside of the bar and up the stairs, which were directly opposite. Between the ends of the bar was a space with two doors, adjacent to the stairs. I passed by the 'window room', where a few German officers were relaxing, and up the step to the main larger room. There were a few civilians in this room, and two or three Germans of other ranks in uniform, plus one other at the bar.

I sat down at a table where two civilians sat and which had two vacant seats. I relaxed my shoulders as I sat down, not as straight as I usually do. There was music, sounded like a radio playing at the rear of the room, which took the edge off any formality. I looked around casually. One young German soldier, about my age, was sitting two tables in front of me on the right and nearer to the bar. The rest of the patrons were behind me. I thought 'Ah well, this is easy!' The German uniforms did not faze me, thanks to the familiarity training that I had completed in the UK.

The soldier at the bar turned around with his drink and came back towards my table. Then, with a little apprehension on my part, he came and seated himself right next to me. I could have done justice to a Cognac at this juncture! He was a more mature soldier than the other one. Also, he did not have a high collar. There was something different in his uniform, - a 'padre' or other order. I should say he was in his 30's. Then I realised that it must have been his seat originally, when he had gone to order his drink at the bar, and he was just returning to it.

Everyone seemed to be listening to the radio music. Then it stopped, accompanied by a few claps and noises which suggested happiness at its demise. The young soldier sitting forward, turned around and, grinning to my adjacent soldier, made some facetious remark, which I guessed was something like, "Who's your nice looking friend?" The older one turned, grinning likewise, to look at me. I grinned back at him and also at the younger one, which made them both laugh. I presume, thinking that with me laughing I had also understood, or guessed, the nature of the remark. They obviously weren't used to Frenchmen understanding them, or being friendly, and I could see that they both appreciated the shared fun.

Whilst this was going on, Olive suddenly appeared at the bottom of the stairs, gave me a quick alarmed glance, then went past the bar out into the street. I looked past her, through the open door, into the square and saw a squad of soldiers disembarking from a lorry. As Olive moved out, so a German officer entered the café and barked out some kind of order in German. The Germans suddenly stood up to leave. Everything seemed to be happening so fast, and so was my mind. As they were preparing to move, I quickly went to the younger soldier, who was smoking, and gestured to him for a light from his cigarette. He quickly obliged and, resuming our grinning - the three of us still full of mirth - passed by the officer near the door and into the street. I fully expected to be barred from leaving and felt his intense gaze as we passed him.

I turned left as instructed by Olive, but with consternation as they both turned left with me. I think they were about to try and converse with me, when three soldiers came around the corner with greetings to my companions. They stopped to talk with a friendly wave to me. During the 75 metre walk I felt very pleased with myself now that I was 'working'. Although the adrenalin was obviously flowing, my brain was active and calculating and I knew I could cope. Fast reactions in the mind dictates what physical action, if any, should be taken.

I supposed the two Germans would joke to the other three about their new found friend. I did notice, as we parted company, a quizzical, humorous smile from the other three and no doubt they would all have a laugh at my expense. Little did they know that an Anglais had just slipped smartly through their fingers. He who has the last laugh!

I found the green door and went inside, to be suddenly hugged by Olive on the other side, who questioned, "How on earth did you get away so soon? I saw the truck load of soldiers appear whilst I was upstairs and saw the officer coming across the square. That's why I 'hi-tailed' it out with my warning glance. Did you have to show your pass? What did they ask you?"

I put my hand up to slow her questioning and told her what had happened. She stared at me in utter disbelief. "My God Oliver, on your first outing! Your first experience, that was brilliant! Such quick thinking, weren't you afraid?"

I laughed, "Me? Afraid? Of course not. I was scared stiff!"

We had another hug and a laugh then she said, "We will stay a while, until things have settled down outside, before we leave. The diagram is not rolled like it was supposed to be, because it might resemble a gun barrel. We will have to take it flat."

The light was beginning to fade, due to the waiting time delay, so we decided we had better move out.

We left by the rear door of the house into the road, parallel to the one we had used to enter. It was gradually getting darker, so we decided to hurry up and get a move on.

Olive wasn't very happy at carrying the flat diagram. She did not like altering arrangements which had previously been set. "I could have carried it vertical by my side, it is not a large item. Now it is more noticeable, like carrying a small picture." She would not let me carry it. "It could create more problems if you were carrying it and were stopped for questioning".

It was really dusk now and we were on the edge of town, about to approach our 'home' road. Then we heard the approach of a military patrol; the local Garrison patrol. Olive looked around for somewhere to ditch the picture. Quick as a flash, I pushed her up against some old rickety wooden railings, across the grass verge. "Put it up your skirt quickly." I said.

"No!" she exclaimed, "I can't hold it there!"

I pushed the map up under her skirt. "Quick, put your arms around my neck" I stated forcefully, as I faced her. Then, keeping my hand up her skirt, held the bottom edge of the picture from falling down. She had her arms around my neck.

31

"For God's sake don't lean back!" I insisted. The wooden railings looked as though they might have replaced iron ones which probably had been removed to be melted down. They looked very rickety.

We must have looked like a courting couple, with me having amorous intentions. If we had stayed much longer in that position, I probably would have had! We were both breathing quite hard and could feel our hearts beating.

The small Garrison patrol approached and then marched past with cat calls and whistles. 'Wow! Thank God for that!' The ruse had worked. A few minutes later we were striding back to the barn. Olive was quiet and I knew she must have been deep in thought, so I didn't interrupt.

When we arrived at our alcove, Olive turned to me and said, "Twice your quick reactions have been quite remarkable. I would love to have you here as part of the group. If only you could speak fluent French it would be so perfect. I'm sorry that the day did not go according to plan. I thought it would be a nice, quiet trip for you to familiarise yourself with the surroundings. A sort of beginner's trip. I'm truly sorry Oliver, it was very much my fault that you could so easily have come to grief. It was one in a million that they decided to check that café and at that time. You must stay in here all day tomorrow. The following day will be very important."

After a pause, Olive continued, "You arrived here a little earlier than expected and we weren't properly prepared. We hadn't got a background for you so, the day after tomorrow, you shall have one."

I dutifully remained in the barn and, two days later, we journeyed into the town centre once again to a bookstall/green grocery/grocer shop. I was introduced to Maurice, the owner, who was to be my official employer. If I was ever asked where I received money from to live on, I would be able to quote

32

him. I would always buy my cigarettes from him. His younger brother John, a thinner replica of Maurice, grew vegetables to supply the shop, and I was employed as a casual labourer for both of them. Maurice was in his fifties; almost bald; small in stature; small moustache and affable; typical grocer, complete with apron. We shook hands, with a nice grip, and I thought, 'Yes, a brave, determined man.'

We then moved down the road to my official residence to meet my landlord. Not a well man, he was thin and pale; brownish hair; thirtyish, in a tweedy-type comfortable suit. He gave me a welcome smile and, again, a handshake. He spoke at length with Olive; obviously they knew each other very well. So now I had a background, and would be able to answer the simplest questions which might be asked.

As we walked back to the barn, I realised how vulnerable I had been with no answers to simple questions, such as; "Where do you live and work?" 'God, it doesn't bear thinking about!' I could have been caught on my first day out if I had been detained in the café, irrespective of all the precautions I had taken.

I asked Olive what she and my landlord had been discussing at length in the flat. "Well, it is just that, if the gendarmes visit him to enquire about residents, he would contact me (Olive) and you would then go to the local police station to verify. It's a very outside chance, paying a visit, but it is better to bear it in mind. Also, if a German official, or army personnel visited, it could well be that they were on to you. Don't concern yourself. It is a very, very remote possibility."

We arrived home at the barn. I reflected on my second 'outing' and thought I had done quite well. I had behaved naturally and had felt quite calm, with no nerves. I had remembered what I had been taught. I didn't stare at anything, including army personnel. I had also remembered to look left

33

and not right when crossing the road. That would be a real give away. Yes, in a way I was feeling quite cocky once again; quite confident in fact. If only I could get on and do whatever I was sent out to do.

CHAPTER 5

I had perused the diagram layout and was now awaiting Henri. It was all damn waiting and I was feeling so scruffy. I think Olive knew this. She seemed to sense things. She got up from the straw and went down the barn to converse with one of the group. She seemed to be making a determined statement. They went out of the barn and returned after fifteen minutes.

Olive came up the barn to me and said, with a smiley face, "Can you walk with your eyes closed Oliver? I could hold your hand to guide you."

I said, "Whatever for? What prank is this dear Olive?" grinning, of course.

"Would you like a nice bath, in hot water, and a shave? I've also got some scissors, if that might help."

"Oh yes…" I said, "I'll even walk on my hands!"

I promised that I would definitely keep my eyes tightly closed. Half an hour later, I was in a galvanised or tin bath, with hot water. The soap was a bit dodgy but it worked. Looking in the mirror, I looked so gaunt and white beneath my beard which had grown quite extensively, but in small tight curls, not stubbly. 'Mmm.' I thought, and debated briefly to keep it on. I say briefly, because that is all it was.

I put on clean clothes. I normally did change every two days when everything was washed. I think shirts were pooled because I often had a strange shirt, but they all fitted me and were always nice and clean. When I came out, Olive gave me a wolf whistle. "What a difference! You look positively human, not like a gorilla anymore!" she laughed, teasingly.

I had been blindfolded, of course, so that I would not be able to identify the helping house if I was caught. I felt like I had been born again, so alive and ready to go.

This feeling was very much with me when Henri came later. His choice of action, i.e. cross connecting on the distribution point outside, limited the choice so much. I reiterated, quite forcefully, that the choice would be so much greater if done inside the exchange. He resented me pushing my method and I could see he was becoming irritated.

Olive suddenly intervened. "Oliver, you do not understand the whole picture!" Then, looking at Henri, "We must tell him."

"No!" replied Henri.

"I insist!" argued Olive.

"You are the boss," said Henri, quickly subdued by Olive's semi-fiery attitude.

I thought, 'The boss? Olive, the boss?'

Then she said to me "We have discovered that the maintenance officer inside the exchange has cousins in the German army. Nobody in the group knows this, except us. He is very much a suspect. If he were to discover what was happening right under his nose and pass on his discovery to the Germans, they would be able to capture the whole group with that information. We cannot risk him discovering the connection even if, as you say, it is such a very small risk."

I apologised to Henri, acknowledging that, if I had known the facts, I would have understood. He was smiling before I had finished apologising, which surprised me to have been 'forgiven' so quickly.

We then decided on one location and left Henri to sound out the occupants of the property.

When we returned to our quarters, I remarked to Olive about Henri's speedy forgiveness. "The reason he mellowed so quickly Oliver, was your French. It amuses him and I think adheres you to him. He just loves to hear your French." She said this with a glint in her eye.

"I will do the pole cross connection when Henri has sorted things out."

"Oh, no Oliver..." said Olive, "the local linesman will do that. He is one of our members and is very pro De Gaulle."

"Olive, what the hell am I doing here? Not taking an active part in what I have come out here to do!"

She came over and put her arms around me. "Don't get all uptight and upset Oliver. You sorted out the available numbers. You also told us the option of inside or outside. It was a pity that the internal engineer was not to be trusted, otherwise we would have got you in there to do the work."

I thought that she was just calming me down at first, then I sensed by her demeanour that she was holding something back. I looked into her eyes and she said, "What is it Oliver?"

"Something's not right Olive, I can tell. You are holding something back from me."

"Yes" she said, "We think alike don't we? As though we are both tuned into the same wavelength. I must admit that, although we haven't known each other very long, we seem to understand each other." She then gave me an extra squeeze, "Let's sit down, I have got to talk to you."

We sat down in the straw opposite each other, but before she could say anything, I stated, "You are more than just a courier aren't you Olive?"

A real, deep sort of smile came over her face as she said, "Yes Oliver I am, as you say, a bit more than just a courier. I gathered that you had worked that out." A pause, then she continued. "I was instructed not to tell you the following information until your 'so called' apprenticeship is over. However, as far as I am concerned, and I do make most of the decisions around here, I have now decided that the time is ripe." Then, looking so very fierce, she proclaimed. "I am here on the spot and I know! Yes, I damn well know! It is I who will judge you."

I thought 'Cor! The Latin/Spanish aspect of her makeup is on show.' I had not seen it up to now and wondered what had sparked that into fire?

Calming down, her eyes watering, she said, "You are more than ready. You have adapted and settled in so quickly. Initially, London wanted you here as soon as possible. You coming here, they hoped would speed things up in case the local technicians or correct persons were unavailable. That much I know. Also, it was part of your apprenticeship. If you had fallen down or lost your nerve during this period of activity, I would hopefully have got you back rather than lose you to the enemy.

"As you now know Oliver, I would hate to lose you, and I will do my utmost to keep you safe. I have grown very fond of you."

"Yes Olive, I feel the same about you. I admire your courage." Then, in a serious tone, "Olive please tell me what the hell am I here to actually do? Do you know?"

She suddenly stood up, her face clouding over somewhat. "Yes Oliver, I do know." Her tone changed again, smiling, she continued, "Hopefully we are going to be here working together for a very long time. I'm so glad you did not have to go back. You have more than proved yourself whilst you have been here." She paused, as if planning her next sentence then, reaching out, held my hand and said, "Yes, it will be dangerous..." slowly, "your primary function will be communication sabotage, involving selected targets, which will be given to us prior to the expected allied invasion."

We both fell silent. Her silence, I suppose, was to let it all sink in. I thought of the implications. 'No quick return for me now. I'm really up to my neck in it now aren't I? It's the real time to be scared of the very obvious danger ahead.' For a second time I truly thought, 'I'm really up to my neck in it now. Will I be going out with the group and taking part in their activities?'

So much for 'Baldy' and 'Blue Suit's' no violence etc.. I inwardly smiled and thought how naive I had been to believe it. Well, so be it! At least I know what I will be doing now, which is a great relief, and I'm quite capable of playing my part. I joined up to fight the war and that is what I will be doing, just like everyone else. I thought of all the adrenalin once again, and how I mustn't get paranoid about the stuff. 'Yes Oliver, throw yourself into it now! What the hell?! Now you can be all positive once again.'

I had been so immersed in my thoughts that I had momentarily forgotten that Olive was present. I looked up and said "Sorry Olive, I was miles away in my thoughts."

She asked, smiling, "You've sorted it all out Oliver?"

"Yes," I said, "I belong now and know what I have to do."

"You will be more stabilized now. I knew you were on edge, the not knowing was beginning to gnaw at you wasn't it?"

"Yes, but that has gone. Now Olive, because I am part of the group, I must ask you to explain a few points in my jigsaw puzzle. For instance, my car journey whilst coming here seemed very frivolous at the check points."

"Oh that!" said Olive.

"And the noise by the gang unloading the Lysander; yet my companions were so different."

Olive was smiling broadly now, almost laughing. "Why the humour Olive?"

I was beginning to be amused, only because she was.

"Well" she said, "There weren't any Germans near the landing site, that is why there was so much noise. Your companions, they were different, very different. They belong to another group; my dedicated elite professionals. They know their job. They are very clinical and can be more than ruthless if the occasion demands it. The check points are staffed by gendarmes, who are mostly in our pockets, but it only needs one bad apple in the barrel. Occasionally, there is a German presence, so we have to be very careful. The Germans cannot be everywhere; there would not be enough men to do the fighting on the front line. Our town Garrison personnel are not members of the great cream of the German army. You can tell just by looking at them! Is that all Oliver, any more questions?"

"No Olive, all done!"

A couple of days passed and Olive had been out and about. I was feeling very secure now, the whole organisation seemed so efficient. She came in and asked, "How would you like to go on your first sortie?"

"Love to! When?"

"Tonight." replied Olive.

"Oh yes." I said "Where to?"

"Just a sortie." she said, "Just to get you primed. You will leave during the night so get a little rest. I will get you something to eat and drink before you go." Then, with a twinkle in her eyes and a smiley face, "Mon brave Anglais!" blew me a kiss and went down the barn.

I did not sleep. Olive came with a meat pastry and a coffee laced with Cognac. "Thought you might like a treat" she said. "You are going to raid a compound. We think there is something worth stealing. Actually, small arms ammunition, which will come in very handy. Just go along with the others and follow their lead."

After refreshments, one of the group called out to say that the time had arrived to leave. We both stood up and Olive kissed me saying, "Good luck Oliver, I will be here when you get back."

I went outside to where a car was waiting. There was also a van. I got into the car. Six of us squeezed in. The van was all closed up and ready to go, so off we went.

I briefly wondered if I could possibly run out of adrenalin and what the effect would be? I settled with the others and tried to join in the Ribald talk, making them laugh with my French. I was 'Anglais' to them and they were 'Frenchies' to me. The longer we went on the road, the more I felt I was becoming part of the group. There was much laughter in the crowded car and B.O. was paramount!

Eventually, the van in front started to slow down and we followed suit. The laughter gradually subsided into utter silence as we came to a halt. We stayed for about 10 minutes; the driver of the van got out and opened his rear door. There looked to be a lot of men inside. Two of them jumped down and walked away in the direction of our travel. The 'Frenchie' next to me whispered that they were going to 'see to' the guard and the guard dogs.

A little while later, we all alighted from the vehicles, having received the signal to do so. After a few hundred yards, we came to a property surrounded with barbed wire fencing; mainly, I think, designed to stop petty thieving. There was a small stone built building nearest the fence. The farmhouse appeared to be in the background. It was very dark and very quiet. I saw two of the group with what looked like rolled up carpet. I thought, 'what the hell have they got there?'

When we arrived at the fence, the two burly characters carrying it threw it until it draped over the fence. I could hardly stop myself from laughing. It was a carpet! One by one, we went over it into the property. It wasn't far to the stone building. It was so very quiet - no sound coming from the group — as small, firm boxes were passed down the line. Not like the fire buckets of old, because there was not enough of us for that. No, we had to walk to each other to collect the booty. It was all so beautifully organised.

Whilst this had been going on, the van had been pushed all the way up to the fence and was being loaded. As we got to the van, two of the men were grinning, holding two ordinary cardboard boxes. They had been opened. One contained ladies very fine and delicate underwear; the other contained what appeared to be wine and sherry glasses, all beautifully packed.

With such a good sized labour force, we retrieved the carpet, stowed it into the van, turned the van around and easily pushed it back to the parked Citroen and off we went.

As we travelled back to the barn, I thought to myself (yet again), how I had loved the action. Something positive, with an element of danger. What I, and many others like me, had joined up to do. I also considered my thoughts regarding the group when first encountering them in the barn. How things had gradually turned around into a feeling of admiration and 'esprit de corps'.

Soon we were back. We stopped at the barn and two men alighted with me, carrying the two cardboard boxes. Olive was waiting and accepted them. They glanced my way, winked, both smiling broadly and, nodding at the boxes, went to join the others in the vehicle. With that, they were gone!

"Oliver, you look so happy. Have you enjoyed yourself?" asked Olive, having sidled up next to me.

"Immensely!" I replied.

I lifted the two boxes and we returned to our quarters at the end of the barn. We squatted down and opened the two boxes. Her eyes lit up as she peered into the 'undies' box. "Marie, my girlfriend at the café, she will love these. We both will. I've not much use for these though" she reasoned, on opening the box containing the glasses.

"They are absolutely beautiful Olive. Such fine, paper thin glasses. I would love to own these. They really are beautiful, however, it is not realistic to keep them. I don't live here." With that, I closed the box.

"You really like these so much don't you?" whispered Olive.

"Yes I do. What will become of them? It will be such a shame to destroy them." It really didn't seem fair.

"I will take these 'undies' to Marie and we shall keep your glasses in the escape tunnel. You never know Oliver. We won't destroy them until we have to. We'll hide them now." Then, both crawling to the hatch, Olive pulled the straw back to expose quite a broad tunnel, the inside of a massive pipe. "There! Voila!" exclaimed Olive, as she pushed them inside the tunnel. We pushed back the straw and sat down.

After Olive had been to see Marie, we settled down for the following night. Reflecting during the night, or early morning, as you might now know, is a habitual thing on my part. I thought about the previous twenty-four hours and listed in my thoughts, lots of questions to put to Olive the next day. I also considered how one can soon adapt and accept situations. I was quite happy sleeping fully clothed, on a bed of straw, with Olive for company. Not quite so happy with the basic cold water therapy every day! I vowed that I would never turn down

43

the offer of a lovely hot bath from anyone during the rest of my time on earth. I would certainly excuse anyone who had the odd B.O. problem. As for a beard by choice? No, not for me! Might be different having a curly beard, but no, it's not me, and one never knows what might eventually nest in there!

There was something I admired about Olive. She always had a sense of humour, even on the darkest day, and in her attitude, not anything specific.

Next morning, after our croissants, I confided in Olive. "I've got a lot to ask you this morning Olive." Her quizzical, mischievous look, as I said it, lifted me to reciprocate in style. "When the Germans discover their guard and dogs dead and the ammunition gone, won't there be a hue and cry and possible repercussions?"

"Oh Oliver, you do let your imagination run wild don't you? Who said we had killed the guard and dogs?"

"I just assumed that the two members had done it."

"No! No!" she responded, "Just listen to me." She had the look of a benevolent school teacher explaining to a kindergarten pupil.

"The place we raided was a requisitioned farmhouse property; the residence of the Colonel. He is going on leave in two days' time, to Germany, to see his wife and family. He is just about packed and ready to go. The operation has been planned to coincide with it. I will take you through it. You all arrived a few minutes early to witness the guard change. We did not want any interruption during our proceedings.

"After the guard had changed, a member of another group, who was a German anti Nazis, approached the guard in uniform. His story was that he had missed the transport back to the site. He did not wish to kill a fellow German; it was the regime he hated. He immobilised the sentry, gagged and trussed him up; supplied with a rope, which the second

44

member of the team had with him, following up behind. He was an ex-veterinary surgeon who also drugged the dogs with a food concoction. The rifle was not stolen, but left with the soldier. who was guarded throughout the operation. We have gambled that the Colonel will not make an issue out of it. Do you think that he would jeopardise his leave to see his family for some boxes of ammunition, which could easily be accounted for? Hardly, but I bet he is hopping mad at not being able to take the 'undies' home to his wife, or girlfriend, and getting just reward. He would not be able to gloat to his friends about his stolen wine glasses from France either! So you see Oliver, we are not just cut throats," and chuckling, she teased, "Well, not all the time!

"We have bags of ammunition now and I have my 'undies and hopefully you have your wine glasses."

With this, my mind was at rest; at least for now.

CHAPTER 6

Although I had been living on my nerve endings since leaving the U.K. I was beginning to feel a little more secure and complacent now. Especially after taking part in the farmhouse compound raid. I felt more relaxed and confident, but with a certain amount of foreboding, knowing that the future would be highly dangerous and risky and most probably short lived. I would be armed and, if caught in possession of a weapon, it would be curtains for me. Yet, it was something positive that I could live with. So, it was in that positive, optimistic and complacent mood that I dropped off to sleep the night after my first 'outing'.

A noisy shouting was entering my brain, "Allez! Allez! Allez vous!" I was up like a shot! I was always the first person to put my feet on the deck when an air raid siren sounded, whilst in the Home Guard. Olive was also vertical.

I immediately collected the two enamel coffee mugs and opened the escape hatch. Olive was moving the straw around to cover up our sleeping area. I moved into the tunnel, pushing the box of wine glasses as far back as possible. Stupidly, I attempted to turn around; I hated the thought of not being able to face the threat. However, the most important thing was that the exit to the hedge/field needed force to push it out if needed and, of course, feet and legs were strongest. I nearly disconnected my neck during the turning around manoeuvre! The tunnel was built to accommodate just Olive and wasn't designed to accommodate a guest.

Of course, Olive came in backwards, pulling the thin rope and straw to cover the entrance, then tightly wound it onto a wooden bar.

This was the routine we had talked about, but had never actually done. No actual rehearsal. I now felt like the rear part of the pantomime horse, only very much closer! Olive had reversed back on to me, squashing my face in order to get in. I couldn't move again to jockey my position because silence was now imperative. I could hear German voices very close. Also, the 'Frenchie' voice of the very essential night watchman. Meanwhile, Olive's bottom was pressing on my face. The voices seemed very close to the entrance now and there was a lot of shuffling and grunting. I could feel my heart pounding, trying to use up some more adrenalin. I suppose poor old Olive's was also. Even in the tortuous moment, I couldn't help gathering a mischievous, funny thought, that I would never get closer to Olive than I am now!

The Germans were taking a long time just outside the entrance. I suppose it was because it was an alcove. I was beginning to feel somewhat apprehensive now; no doubt Olive would be feeling the same. They went away and I could hear them much further in the distance. They returned, accompanied by a new voice. The entrance shook, as though a boot had been applied to it. After a few more minutes, the voices faded out. It all fell silent. After a while, Olive whispered. "Stay quiet and still." As if I was going to make a noise now!

Eventually, we heard some 'Frenchie' voices and the entrance was pulled back. Olive untied the rope and we crawled out on 'all fours', to be welcomed with friendly grins. Olive immediately thanked them and praised them for their alertness at sounding the alarm. Needless to say, we all stayed awake and alert until daybreak.

During the day, there was much activity. 'Frenchies' were moving in and out of the barn. Olive left for about an hour 'to see what was going on.'

Eventually she returned with her usual smiley face. She flounced in saying, "It's ok, the panic is now over! They were not targeting our barn specifically. The search seemed to have

47

been organised to include all possible properties in an effort to find the stolen goods, not the thieves."

Changing the subject, Olive told me, "It's the first time I have ever had to use the tunnel. I'm so sorry that I had to sit on you."

"I did not mind one bit." I giggled.

"No, I bet you didn't!" she retorted, grinning. "You are encroaching Oliver. First, the fence and diagram episode, and now this. I will have to keep a special eye on you, in case you manipulate a further encroachment." Yes, it was all foolish talk and good fun.

As you know, she often called me 'Mon brave Anglais', so I decided to reciprocate in style. On the next occasion, I called her, 'My brave, petite Pyrenean.' She was very amused and I could see she was happy when I called her that.

One morning, after all the excitement had died down, Henri appeared to tell us that all was now going well. The listening telephone had been installed, together with the interpreter. I could now get on with the 'serious stuff', or so I thought, but no, it was not to be. Later, I was told the interpreter had decided to become awkward. He said that the Communist resistance group should be given the information which was being received. It was pointed out to him, by Henri, that the less people who knew about it the more secure the project would be. He later asked for more money, to keep himself from informing the Communists. Initially, Henri agreed to pay him and so prevent everything becoming a catastrophe.

Olive and Henri were now gradually including me in some of the envisaged projects; one of which was a fuel storage depot. I felt that I belonged more in the group. I also paid the odd visit into the town on my own, mostly to see Maurice and his store, to buy the odd commodity. Olive was more than a little worried about it. I said that I was sitting about too much and it wasn't good for me. I needed more activity. I just wanted to be me. I was getting more confident now and wanted to feed myself with more confidence.

Olive stressed that I would be needed later, which was most important. "I don't want to lose you beforehand Oliver. In fact, I don't want to lose you at all."

Looking convinced, I replied, "Yes, you are quite right as always Olive, I must cut down my journeys and be a good boy." I said it just to pacify her. I did not want Olive to worry on my account; she had enough worries and stress to cope with. However, my intentions remained the same.

We sat down to work out the assault on the fuel depot, accompanied by two more 'Frenchies'; experts in their own field of explosives.

There was a Spaniard sitting in and, although he was a Spaniard, he had lived in the area of the depot for many years and was very well acquainted with the geographical area. He was a likeable man; very short; in his twenties or early thirties; dark hair and flashing eyes, which darted this way and that way. He laughed easily, and yet could also be sad. I gathered that he had some family loss in Spain during the Spanish civil war, when the Luftwaffe intervened, so he had no love for Hitler's Germany.

We had to try and make the result of the operation look like an accident, to prevent the possibility of reprisals; especially on the civilians in the area.

About a week later, whilst we were at the table, one of the group of 'Frenchies' appeared quite agitated. He told us that the interpreter had been killed in a road accident. I was horrified. Not just because he had been killed, I didn't know him, but that our project had been severely interrupted.

49

I looked at Olive and Henri. They both registered alarm on their faces after hearing the news.

Immediately, I knew something was wrong. My mind was very efficient. It had been so tuned since I came here. It had to be. I now analysed everything that entered my head. Suspicion took the place of alarm and, as I looked at Olive's face and then Henri's, I knew.

I demanded, "Why?" They looked at each other then back at me. "Why?" I repeated forcibly.

Olive responded. "It is the war Oliver; it is the war mon Cher!"

"Oui!" added Henri, nodding his head, "C'est la guerre!"

Later, as we both sat down in the alcove, Olive protested, "It's no use looking at me like that Oliver, it had to be done! It just had to be done to protect the group, the projects and all the things we are fighting for. I have said before today, that it only needs one bad apple in the barrel. Well, we have taken it out now and that will make us much safer."

I thought, 'My God, it's so clinical. So matter of fact!' I returned, "What about the project now Olive? We don't have an interpreter!"

"What do you mean we don't have an interpreter?" said Olive, annoyed.

"Because you have just removed him from this earth!" I exclaimed, incredulously.

"Oh Oliver." she laughed. "My dear, dear Oliver, blame it on your French. It just has to be. You do keep us so amused." She continued, after a moment laughing. "It wasn't the interpreter; it was the owner of the property who was the problem. The interpreter is fine; a real De Gaulle man. The owner, or should I say, ex-owner was the problem. He became too inquisitive and realised that he had found a way to increase

50

his income by blackmailing us. We don't tolerate threats Oliver. When action is needed it is done. So be it. I have no regrets. None what-so-ever!" She emphasised this last statement.

Observing her face, I certainly believed her. She had been in the resistance business for a long time and had honed her efficiency to a fine degree. There was no hint of mercy in those eyes.

As a newcomer, I would have to get used to the merciless attitude, and to think and act accordingly, if I wished to stay alive. I was trained to kill in combat or to achieve an objective in war. I suppose it could well be the same; we were threatened and the threat had to be eliminated. It just had to be! It was the cold blooded method and the fact that he wasn't the official enemy, that troubled me. He was a French man for God's sake and yet he was a very great security risk to us all. Reluctantly, I just had to agree with Olive. She was right. French, German or Italian it did not matter. Their life or ours is what it amounted to. As Olive said earlier "It's the war Oliver!"

I looked up at Olive, she had a most concerned and anxious look on her face, her eyes riveted on mine. "Well?" she said, aggressively. "You do take your time don't you? Do you, or don't you agree?"

"Yes, I do take my time when it is necessary, but I do agree with you Olive. Yes, I do now, whole heartily agree with you."

She answered me with a beaming smile, and leaned across to hug me. "Thank God for that..." a moment, then, "I'll get us some coffee." As she retreated, turning her head, she winked at me saying, "and some Cognac!"

CHAPTER 7

Dutifully, I stayed in for a couple of days, abiding by Olive's recent requested advice. Unfortunately, I became bored once again, just sitting about.

I waited for Olive to go out on her many excursions, before venturing out into the town. I just had to. I was a physically active person. I couldn't abide sitting about.

I felt like a naughty boy going against Olive's wishes. I figured the walk into town would do me a world of good; it was also good for me to see Maurice in the shop. I always received a happy welcome. Likewise, from his younger brother, when he was in the shop.

On this occasion, having visited the shop and walking away, I became conscious of a Sergeant and private soldier coming towards me. I 'knew' that I was going to be stopped. To alter course was not an option; that would have aroused their suspicions. They were going to stop me for sure!

A brief thought passed through my mind. 'Olive was right, I am getting too cocky, too sure of myself, taking too many risks. I am an idiot!' It could lead to an early exit from this world.

The Sergeant held out his hand. "Pass!" he demanded.

I stayed calm as I extracted the pass from my pocket. He stared at it with a puzzled look, then showed it to his companion. They muttered something together, accompanied with glances at me. The delay did not do my nerves any good, but I remembered my training. They are your friends. I dutifully smiled, not too much. Suddenly, the Sergeant pivoted on the spot and signalled to a civilian standing at the other side of Maurice's shop.

Immediately, I quickly went through my options. The soldier had now levelled his rifle at my midriff; holding his rifle at hip height, his left hand on the barrel, the right hand not actually on the trigger, but on the trigger guard. 'Hmm' I thought, 'I could take him out using surprise action, by quickly moving the rifle to my left-hand side, which would sway his body to his right, exposing more of his left neck. A nice target for my right hand edge to chop his carotid artery area, with a reverse chop to the Sergeant's right neck.' I knew it would not be sufficient.

The plain clothes officer, now almost on the scene, would probably be wearing a holster and, worse still, an alarm whistle which would quickly bring soldiers to the scene. No, I would have to face it out and smile which, although I had just done so, I now found hard to do so again. Fear of a Gestapo interrogation tensed up my face muscles!

I'm sure my attempted smile ended up looking more like a smirk. The plain clothes character had a cold-blooded face. He was quite tall and stared at me as though I had just crawled out from beneath a stone. 'God!' I thought, 'This is it! I'm so sorry Olive, just so sorry. What a bl*#*y idiot!' He really was a cold fish.

He took the pass and scrutinised it. I saw his eyebrows move up (I did not miss a thing). He glanced at me, then back to the pass. Once again, he returned his stare at me, and with a deathly cold, faint smile, he just nodded and handed the pass back to me.

He spoke to the two soldiers who then broke into smiles. I tried to smile back with the words "Danke Herren." This brought forth an increase in humour, almost laughter, from both of them, plus a friendly pat on my shoulder by the Sergeant, as they left me to continue on their patrol.

'Why was it that, when no matter which language I spoke, whether French or German, it promoted such mirth?' So, over another hurdle. I must admit that I felt a wee bit jittery but, I had submitted my pass and it had been accepted.

Phew! It had been a nerve wracking time, especially during the examination. 'I don't think Olive will be very pleased. Does she need to know? Not really! The only positive side of my 'walkies' was that the pass had been accepted. I am certain she would wish to know that. Oh, but of course, Maurice must have witnessed it, so Olive would soon get to know anyway.' I supposed I would have to accept her broadside with grace and humility.

I decided I would bite the bullet and tell her as soon as I got back to the barn. It would be far more comfortable than having the Gestapo for company!

CHAPTER 8

As I walked into the barn, there she was, Olive, at the far end near our alcove, feet apart, hands on hips in a most aggressive mode. 'Surely', I thought, 'She can't possibly know already! Perhaps she is annoyed that I have been out into the town. If that is the case, God knows what she will be like when I give her some details.' My thoughts were racing ahead of me.

As I approached, I could see her face. She was definitely angry. Her actual words of greeting were, "It bloody well serves you right. It's about time you had a shock to frighten you into being sensible!"

Taken aback, I replied, "You know already then?"

"Of course I do," she retorted, "I know what you are up to before you do! Did you know that the man you saw is the real nasty? He has a terrible reputation. I cannot understand why you were released. He arrests anyone on the slightest suspicion and then they are subjected to a detailed interrogation." She was now speaking very fast and getting visibly stressed. "You wouldn't have lasted very long. They would have beaten everything they wanted to know out of you, until you would have been like a lifeless bit of torn wet bloody rag; then dragged you out and shot you!" Her eyes were becoming quite misty. "Why did he let you go? Why, for goodness sake? What did you say to him?"

"Hold on Olive." I implored, "I'm just getting over my escapade."

"Serves you right!" Biting her lip, retracted this. "No! I didn't mean that Oliver." She then burst into tears, holding her face in her hands.

I stepped forward to hold her shoulders, at the same time as she wound her arms around my waist, resting her head on my chest. We were both quiet for a while.

Having recovered her composure, and still in the same close position, she whispered, "I'm supposed to be very cross and very angry with you. You do not have any idea how I feel do you? I feel so close to you now, as I would be to a younger brother. I can't explain the relief I now feel that you have escaped from what I thought would be the end of you.

"You are a real escape artist. I can hardly believe it. You must have some built in divine gift to protect you." Her voice was stable now as she continued, "I feel responsible for your safety, but remember Oliver, you are now an agent and not a Commando. You do sometimes have to wait around, that is your job! You have got to be more disciplined."

"Yes boss!" I replied, in a cringing voice, which made her laugh. Inwardly, I knew that she was right. I had had a fright to prove it.

CHAPTER 9

I returned - contemplating a quiet existence - once again to the barn, and decided that I would put my time to some good use. With such a lack of exercise, I could develop into an overweight slob. As a result of this thinking, I started an exercise routine to keep me supple and fit; a routine which I have kept to this day in a modified form.

Olive thought it was a good idea, but declined the offer to participate. She now spent a little more time with me in the barn so, consequently, I was more content. The fuel depot project was postponed. From memory. I think it was due to the probability of injuring workers in the area.

Although I exercised, the enforced inactivity in youth, especially when all fired up in a wartime environment, tended to fuel a certain amount of despondency. I was entering into one of those despondent moods one morning when Olive bustled in with, "Get ready Oliver we have to go out Mon Cher!"

Those few words gave a great power lift to my mood. "Brilliant! Where are we going Mon Cherie?"

She grinned on hearing the 'mimic' and, still smiling, replied "We will eat these first and drink the coffee," as she laid the food and drink on the straw.

As we ate, she informed me, "You have to go to your official abode to see the landlord and a gendarme at 11:45 to record your tenancy. You will meet them at the entrance to the property in the first instance, and then probably go inside to complete the registration. If you don't attend in his presence, it would mean a journey to the police station to register. There could be a risk involved, because you might be asked a few questions, especially if the landlord is not present, plus, the fact that a German presence may be there. The gendarme at the residence will be expecting you and understands your situation. I will accompany you for part of the journey, but not to the residence. It is only a formality Oliver, but an important one."

We walked into the town, then went our separate ways. I passed the shop and waved to Maurice's brother. Eventually, I arrived at my official residence, but walked on, suspicious that they were not there to meet me. I did not pause or linger in case there was a problem, but stopped behind a wall further up the road and kept the property under surveillance; thinking of a plan of action if something else developed. There was a sense of relief when first the landlord arrived and then the gendarme on his bicycle. I was very annoyed, because it is essential that timetables must be kept. They surely must have known that? I made sure that they actually met at the residence before I went to meet them.

When I arrived, the gendarme was speaking quite urgently and quickly to the landlord, so much so that I could not understand a word of it. The Gendarme stopped and questioned the landlord as to my identity, then smiled and nodded pleasantly to me.

The three of us entered the house and stayed a short time, whilst the gendarme filled in a form; having to bend over a small table in the hallway. He resumed his urgent fast talking, but now included me in it. I waved my hands to slow him down but, like a characteristic Frenchman, he threw his arms up, quite excitably. I shook my head. They continued to converse with me in a mixture of French and pigeon English, which took some time.

Eventually, I understood what the gendarme was trying to convey. He had heard talk in the station about an Anglais being in the area and it could well be me under suspicion, or even under surveillance. 'How? Why? I wonder if Olive has heard anything'. Inwardly I became somewhat alarmed. I thought about my stoppage in town. Perhaps they had not been deceived by my pass and had rumbled me and were now actually watching me as to what I was up to. I remembered that Olive was very surprised that they had not even questioned me.

Thanking them, I left to return to the barn. I must put them off the scent if it is me that they are after. As I walked down the street, I did some serious thinking. It was then that I sensed that I was being followed! My finely tuned senses? Or perhaps due to the information that I had just received? 'Nothing but bl*#*y stress ever since I had left the UK! If it's not one thing it is another.' It certainly kept me on my toes and honed my senses.

Instead of going directly towards Maurice's shop, I turned off further along the street and came to the alleyway at the rear of the shop, which runs by the side of the shop up to the main entrance. I went up the alleyway then abruptly turned left and into the shop. If anyone was following me, by the time they had traversed the alley, they would not know where I had disappeared to, but would guess that I might be in the shop.

There was one customer in the shop waiting. I walked past him through the inner doorway into a hall, or passage way, and met Maurice carrying something, I presume, for his customer. Before he could speak, accompanied with his cheerful smile, I did a fingers on lips routine and removed his hat from his head - a blackish colour, with a small peak at the front - and put it on my head. I could feel his gaze of bewilderment as I continued down the passage. There was a small room on the left, with a small window to match, which looked out on to the alleyway. It had a massive, large curtain pole across the top of the window, with heavy drapes on either side, leaving the window exposed. I think the curtains were so large that they could have covered half the wall. In the top right-hand corner of the window there was quite a large cobweb. The room looked like a utility room, with a few cardboard boxes and what looked like a small rocking chair as 'occupants'. (The trivial things one remembers.)

I walked on towards the rear entrance and came across a sink in the alcove, on my right, with coats on hooks. I slipped one off its hook and put it on, quickly taking out a few envelopes and bits of paper from the pockets, so that if I did get caught it would not incriminate Maurice. The coat had ample room in it; much better to be a little large than too small. I then ripped a page from a notepad, roughly folding it many times tightly as I approached the small rear door of the shop. I pushed the small wad of paper down the inside of the heel of my right shoe until it was partly under my foot. Just before I opened the door, I took off my spectacles and slipped them into the top pocket of my jacket, then went out on to the rear street. The whole operation must have taken not much more than thirty seconds. Now my shape and appearance had completely changed, and my walking gait likewise, not limping but altered.

'My God what a cap!' I did not realise the size of Maurice's cap until I started walking. A good job I had a decent pair of ears!

I walked normally, no turning around for a quick look as one is tempted to do. I kept walking down the lane towards the barn then, before I got to the barn, I turned right into a narrow road leading to the farm labourers' cottages. I walked the full length of the road, walked around the back of the last cottage out of sight of the road. I stayed for a period of five minutes then turned around and retraced my steps back to the barn lane. Now I would come face-to-face, so to speak, with anyone who might be following me. Not a soul in the small lane except for a farm labourer's wife, hands on hips, complete with apron, looking on with suspicion. The barn lane was also clear, so I turned right and walked up to the barn.

I was immediately accosted by Paul, one of the security men on duty. Paul and myself had developed quite a friendship, always laughing with each other; generally, about his atrocious attempt at English, and of course my imperfect French.

I said a few of my Anglais/French words and watched his face as I spoke. Paul looked very surprised, with an incredulous look on his face, before breaking down with laughter. "Anglais? Anglais? Mon Dieu! Pour quoi?" Laughing at me, he tried to knock my hat off, which he eventually managed to do, and kept hold of it. Such great fun as I entered the barn.

CHAPTER 10

After the horse play with Paul, the Frenchie security guard, I let him keep the hat and gave him the coat as well, telling him that both of them belonged to Maurice. He enquired as to whether I meant Maurice in the shop, and I confirmed. With that, he promised to return them for me. We were both still in a highly amused state.

I was very relieved to take off both the hat and the coat. The hat, because I hate wearing a hat, the coat because it had made me so overheated. So much so that I felt I was 'burning up' inside. I took off my jacket, when I left Paul at the entrance, and walked up the barn towards the alcove, passing the ablutions on my left hand side, casually swinging my coat in my right hand. I saw two 'Frenchies' laughing as I approached them, on my way up the barn. Obviously, they had seen the antics of Paul at the entrance.

It was then that I heard a commotion behind me, coming from the entrance which I had just left. I turned my head on hearing someone shouting "Non! Non!" in a frightened voice. I saw one man disappear into the ablutions, with a heavily built character, in a pale coloured shirt, in pursuit. Paul, the guard, was shouting and running after both of them. I dropped my coat and ran back to the ablutions.

A sorry sight met my eyes. The man who was being chased was slumped with his back against the opposite wall, covered in blood. Paul was standing by the victim's side, his left hand stretched, gripping the large man's right wrist; which held a knife with an 8 inch, bloodied blade. The large man's left arm had a partial grasp of Paul's throat. Paul's right arm was trapped behind the body of the murdered man.

I dived forward and reinforced Paul's grip on the large man's knife hand; pushing it further towards the floor.

He was a very powerful man with an enormous, thick neck. I lunged for his throat with my left hand, squeezing as hard as I could. I could see Paul's face was becoming contorted by the grip on his throat.

I increased the pressure of my fingertips, hoping it would force the large man to release his grip on Paul's throat, hopefully forcing him to drop his knife. It was obvious I was achieving the desired effect from the murderous look that I was now receiving from him.

Suddenly, he released his grip on Paul's throat and moved his left arm. It must have released the body of the dead man, as he suddenly slumped forward, hitting the large man's legs, causing him to lose his balance. In a blink of an eye, the falling body of the dead man released Paul's right arm, which also contained a knife. He swiftly plunged this upwards, into the large man's abdomen; demonstrating a perfect training book exercise. I could hardly comprehend the speed of events. With that, the large man just fell forwards, twisting as he fell towards me, almost knocking me over. I staggered back as he fell forward, down my chest, catching my knees with his head as he did so.

I moved further back to the entrance, surveying the horrible carnage. I looked down at my front. It was saturated in blood. I could feel it on my face.

The 'Frenchies' who were in the barn had now arrived and there were many "Mon Dieu!" exclamations all round.

"Mon Dieu, Anglais!" They thought I had been knifed, because of all the blood on me. They also believed I had used the knife to kill the large man!

After a fiery, instant inquest, containing yet more, "Mon Dieu's!" along with the loud explanations from Paul - all in rapid French - the truth was eventually realised.

Paul was shouting enthusiastically, "Merci! Merci Anglais!"

As I walked from the scene, it occurred to me what a mess the ablutions were now in: The right hand curtain normally screened a wooden box toilet seat over a large bucket. The curtain had been torn down and ripped, together with its light timber pole; which had become dislodged. The wooden seat was drenched with blood. The water tank and the big, heavy stone sink on the side - where very brave souls washed - were also splattered in blood.

It took some time for the tension to subside after the incident.

The 'Frenchies' began to gesticulate and shout to me that it was not my problem. "Not your problem, Anglais!" shouted Paul. "You go now up the barn. It is a French family domestic problem. You go and wait for Margo." (Shortened from Margaret or Margarette, so I was given to understand).

They were not involved with code names.

CHAPTER 11

Olive hurriedly rushed into the alcove, carrying a bucket of water. "My God Oliver..." she said, "What a state you are in. Are you hurt? I was told that you were OK. I'm so grateful to you, and so are the others, for saving Paul's life. You mustn't be involved in this mess. You just cannot be. It would reveal your identity. The gendarmes investigating the murder will be here very soon. They are bound to close the entrance and look into the barn. We will have to go out through the tunnel. One of the 'Frenchies' will be at the exit, with a change of clothes for you. This will enable you to get over to the cottages safely, without the giveaway blood stains. You will have a detailed clean, removing all traces of blood, and a complete change of clothing. Nobody in authority must see you like this; all bloody. It would be curtains for you!" All this, she gabbled as she wiped my face with a wet flannel.

"We must go now, quickly Oliver, before the gendarmes arrive. Hurry, go front first into the tunnel." Then, fixing me with a mischievous look, she giggled, "I will go after you."

Getting down on all fours, I winked. "What a shame. I'll have nothing to look at."

"Precisely!" she smirked.

Moving through the tunnel, I carefully moved my box of wine glasses to one side as, I forcibly opened the exit. As I stood up outside, on to a well-worn path, Olive came up behind me. "Stop, stay still Oliver. There are blood stains still on your shoes." With this, she crouched down and cleaned them off with her handkerchief.

I was looking at a slightly rising field, with a ditch in the foreground. There was a 'Frenchie' at the corner of the barn; I suppose on lookout duty. I quickly changed clothes and exchanged the bloodied ones for the clean ones in the bag. I kept my original coat, which I had rescued from where I had dropped it in the barn. It covered the replacement shirt, which was extra-large! I guessed it was the nearest one to be grabbed in a hurry.

Olive secured both entrance and exit to the tunnel. It would mean that to use the tunnel again, we would have to enter by means of the exit.

We turned right and went down the well-worn path that ran alongside the rear of the barn. The occupants of the cottages used it as a short cut to the bakers. It was the baker from where Oliver procured her croissants etc. It was situated across the road at the other end of the path, just around the bend, on the road which had been used on my original arrival at the barn.

We joined the 'Frenchies' at the end of the path, and the three of us crossed a narrow lane on to another well-worn track, through grassland, to the rear of the cottages. We entered the kitchen of the end cottage. The farmer's wife had filled a tin bath, just like the one that I had used previously. They left me to strip and bathe. What made it more enjoyable was that it was a much larger bath than before.

I was enjoying this heaven sent luxury when the door opened and the farmer's wife peeped around it. She called back, in French, through the doorway, which resulted in Olive entering, carrying a large jug. I couldn't believe it. "Excuse me Oliver, I want to make sure that all the blood is cleaned from your head. Some of it is matted in your hair." Olive asserted, as she scrubbed at my grimy curls.

It could only happen in France. I could not imagine any English girl being so bold; at least not in the 1940s. Another female, with an enquiring voice, piped up from the doorway. "Oui!" answered the farmer's wife and so entered the girl with

66

the voice. 'How many more?' A bath is supposed to be a very private occasion.

She came right up to the tin bath and touched my shoulder, whilst Olive was washing my hair. "Merci Anglais! Merci!" she choked. Then bent down, kissed my soapy head, and departed.

"What was that all about?" I asked, plainly confused.

Olive cut me short, explaining, "That was Paul's wife."

"I understand her reason to thank me, but being an Anglais, I'm just not used to these bath side introductions."

"You should be grateful that you are not standing up!" joked Olive.

Even in tense, hurried, and stressful situations, with one's mind engrossed in planning the next move, and trying to think positive of the immediate future, we managed our bit of fun.

"All done Oliver, you are now in pristine condition! Can you manage to dry yourself?" Olive teased.

"Definitely!" I asserted.

The farmer's wife said something to Olive - in French of course - which made them both burst out laughing. "Au revoir Mon Cher et dépêche-toi!" (Hurry up), and out they went, giggling infectiously.

A little later, now spotlessly clean after my thorough valeting, I entered the other room of the cottage, where a few 'Frenchies' and their wives were gathered. They smiled and clapped their hands as I entered. Olive gave me a second introduction; a visible one now.

Paul's wife kissed me vigorously on both cheeks, saying "Merci, Merci, Anglais!"

Meanwhile, Olive was stuffing pastries and a bottle of fizzy drink into a haversack. Mischievously, she jested, "You can't take advantage of your popularity with the ladies, because we are going for a bike ride." More seriously, she added, "There

67

will be two men riding about a mile ahead of us, and one about half a mile ahead of him, so we will be forewarned of any problems". She gave me a handgun and revealed, "We will be using it soon." I must have looked surprised because she laughed. "It's only a practice Oliver. It's nothing serious! We have to get away from the area for a little while, until the heat is off, so we might as well pass the time with some target practice."

Before we got on our bikes, a little girl, of around six years old, came up to me, stopping a few feet away, holding a shirt in her hand. She just stared at me. I smiled and said, "Bonjour!" She continued staring at me. As she was ushered away, I waved and smiled at her. She reciprocated with a big smile and kept turning around as she was being led away, holding her mother's hand. I never knew who she was, or why the attention.

We cycled across the common land to the local farm road. I felt so happy because I had almost lived on my bike during my youth. However, that is another story.

A few miles along the road, we turned right into a sparsely wooded area. We stopped and lodged our bikes into a thicket. I made a mental note of a funny shaped tree, so as to enable me to locate the place, if needed. We walked quite a long way, until we came to some timber buildings, continuing into a large manmade clearing. Olive told me that it used to be a stopover place for German forces, during their invasion of France. There were many 'Frenchies' to be seen. All strangers to me. All very affable and, of course, very vocal!

Olive handed me the automatic hand gun. It was a very light weapon. Easy to handle for a quick draw and, although it had only .22 bullets, it certainly did a good job on targets. It was for short range use; more for personal protection.

Many years later, in Kenya, during the Mau Mau period, I bought a hand gun for my personal protection and I'm sure the gun was identical. In Kenya, I used high velocity bullets, which were an improvement. Again, that is another story…

We slept on straw mattresses in a hut alongside some other 'Frenchies'; with access to grey army blankets if needed. The ablutions were a little less primitive than the barn as it had a shower. This was fed by gravity from tanks, on the roof, situated in a special ablutions block. It was purely dependant on rainfall. I wasn't aware of this facility until Olive returned, having taking full advantage of it. I assumed she had nipped in there to make sure of a shower before the tank ran dry.

I was so glad that I was ignorant of the existence of the ablution block. Olive had returned, informing me through chattering teeth, "God Oliver, that water is absolutely freezing cold! I've just had a shower and don't recommend it. I'm not having anymore. That is the first and last time! I don't care, I'll wait until I get back to Marie's café." She continued with a burst of laughter, "I'm sure Marie would die under one of those showers! She's not a hardy person."

I thought, but didn't say it, 'neither am I! I'll put that task off as long as possible.' The showers were not as primitive as the barn ablutions, but the knowledge of all the area the freezing cold water would cover didn't bear thinking about! At least the barn facility was only a stone sink and could only be used on selected areas. Olive never failed to surprise me in the things she did.

CHAPTER 12

I awoke suddenly to 'Frenchies' already on their feet shouting, "Anglais! Anglais!" I became vertical almost immediately. "We are being attacked!" was what I was able to comprehend.

Looking around, I couldn't see Olive. 'Where the hell was she? In the toilet block? Maybe!' No one seemed to know where she was. I could hear rifle shots not so far away. All the occupants evacuated the hut; me included. We rushed into the bushes to give us time to evaluate the situation, whilst under cover. Two 'Frenchies' arrived, talking rapidly. It appeared that quite a large number of German troops were evidently coming to the camp; probably to take advantage of its facilities, only to be fired on by some undisciplined French idiots! Now it was time to escape.

I vaguely knew the lay out and direction back to the barn, but 'whereabouts were the troops?' A particularly tubby 'Frenchie' told me that there were a number of paths one could follow, if one turned right near the end of the row of buildings. They all led on to the road we had cycled on. This group of 'Frenchies' would, of course, go to ground in a different direction. I couldn't see any one of my group in the short time available. Therefore, I preferred to be on my own, relying on myself to survive.

The noise and gun fire had now subsided but, that was no help because I didn't know from where the threat would come. I reasoned that the first path would lead on to the road nearest the campsite, which was not what I wanted. I crossed a second path and decided to go down the next path - if there was one -because I didn't know how many paths there were. Fortunately, there was one, and I took it.

I had to be choosy, I didn't want to walk on a path that came on to the road near the camp; I could be walking into trouble. Also, I did not want to come out on to the road beyond the point where I had left my bicycle. I warily trod the chosen path, being very alert for any sign of danger, or noise. It was getting quite light; the beginning of a new day.

I eventually realised that I must have travelled quite a considerable distance and was becoming concerned, beginning to doubt the 'Frenchies' advice. I was also a miserable bunny, thinking about my missed morning coffee and croissant.

Suddenly, I came upon a large hole in the ground - possibly a bomb crater – and, what appeared to be, a tin helmet. I suddenly realised that it was a German steel helmet and, a German soldier was in there in the crater! I went for my automatic, and was prepared to use it, but saw that the German had slipped down the side of the crater, and was unarmed. As I approached him, I could see that he was quite agitated, especially so because of the gun that I held in my hand. I also saw that his rifle was at the bottom of the crater, out of his reach, and that he had a damaged leg.

I jumped into the crater, with my mind working overtime. I retrieved his rifle and ejected the cartridges. Thinking, at the same time, that I could use this situation to my advantage, should I get captured; which was highly probable. Taking stock of him, I guessed he was about my age; fairish hair, showing near the side of his helmet. Despite the obvious high level of fear showing, he had a pleasant face.

'Damn this war! In a warless world, we could be enjoying a pint and having fun now.' I thought to myself.

I put my fingers to my lips, returned his rifle to him, then forcibly grinning, took out my pass and showed it to him. It took a little while for him to understand the contents. He then smiled, through the pain in his leg, as it dawned on him that I

71

was not unfriendly. I gently patted him on the shoulder and left quickly. The whole scene, enacted, had taken under two minutes. I was concerned that someone would be looking for him.

My strategy was that, if I was captured, the soldier's experience would confirm the validity of the pass and, hopefully, I could escape a dreaded interrogation with the Gestapo, which would mean curtains for me! They would have to get a Latvian interpreter to do so.

I moved on down the path, still very tense, reflecting what a devious sod I had become. When I came to the road junction, I kept well into the path cover and surveyed the road. In the distance, slowly coming towards me on the road, from the direction of the barn, were two German soldiers, one on each side of the road. Further back, more troops in single file on each side of the road, inspecting the bushes. I could see that they were members of an efficient fighting force, unlike the garrison troops.

As they came slowly nearer, I presumed that the two leading soldiers were acting as scouts and, if attacked, the main body of troops would have a target to deal with.

I realised that I would have to make myself scarce. I trod on selected areas of growth and gradually moved into the bushes, dragging a lot of fern and grass over me, behind the bushes. I went to ground amongst the wet undergrowth, made myself as comfortable as possible, kept still, and waited.

I wondered what action would be taken on the discovery of the soldier, and his account of our meeting.

A little while later, I heard the approach of what I thought were two soldiers. They passed by. The reaction was not long in coming. Through the debris, I saw the middle half of two soldiers returning from where they had come. A pause, and a few German words. One of them stopped nearby, the other went on. 'Oh, for goodness sake, why stop here?' I soon realised that he had stopped to have a crafty smoke. A few minutes elapsed, more troops came on the scene. I didn't know how many. I gathered that they must have been medical corps personnel. A little later they returned - I presumed with the casualty - back to the road. The soldier, who had stayed for a smoke, appeared unnervingly close for comfort. His mate joined him once again, for a few words. Their questioning voices were probably discussing the soldier's account. I couldn't see them, but hoped they would soon push off. The thought of them staring in my direction gave me even more cause for concern.

The ground dampness was gradually making progress through my clothes, and my face was itching. No matter how much I wrinkled and moved my nose, and face, it would not go away! I started twitching and jokingly hoped it wouldn't be permanent. I chastised myself immediately for letting my mind wander.

Suddenly consternation, one of the soldiers decided to relieve himself. I could hear the splashes very close! I expected any second now to be captured. After what seemed an age, they moved back towards the road.

I stayed very still for a long time after they had gone. They might well try the trick of moving away, then stopping to silently watch for any movement; just as submarine and hunter surface vessels did on the sea.

Eventually, I moved very slightly so that I could see the path and surrounding bushes, through parted grass. I got up, feeling almost paralysed down one side. Not a soul in sight. I crept, very carefully, the short distance to the road, keeping an eagle eye for any hint of danger. Still not a soul to be seen.

It looked to me that they had now passed through, towards the camp. If the troops were looking for me, they would naturally assume that I would head away from the camp, the way we had come on the bikes. Although I could be walking back into danger by going towards the camp, it was, in fact, the opposite to what the soldiers would expect. I kept well into the side. 'Where were the bikes and that tree? Were they in front or behind me?' Movement was warming up my legs and side. 'What would I give for a nice bucket of coffee and a croissant?!'

'What the hell had become of Olive?' We had developed such a close bond towards each other. I felt so upset and fearful for her. A common bond of wartime danger fuelled it. I disciplined my mind to ignore my feelings and concentrated on staying alive. 'Everything will evolve and come to a conclusion, whether it be heaven or hell!'

Suddenly, I met 'Onion Face' from Brittany. I saw his big, ruddy face, grinning at me from inside the bushes. "Anglais! Mon amie! Bonjour!" he shrieked, surprised to see me.

After a gleeful meeting, and enduring his unique onion aroma - he excitably wished to hug and kiss me on both cheeks - I enquired about Olive. "Is she safe?"

"Oui, Oui! She is ok and frantic about your safety." He reassured me.

I asked where she was. He pointed up the road, towards the camp, on the opposite side. He informed me she was there, but maybe she had gone now. "I will come with you Anglais. The Germans have gone through and taken possession of the camp." He spoke in hushed tones.

Soon, I recognised the tree. 'Brilliant! I know where I am, and Olive is safe.' I went into the bushes. No bikes! No Olive! 'What now?'

It was then that a Frenchie appeared. I think his name was Henri - another Henri - not unlike the original one; a very

74

talkative type, demonstrative, and fast on his feet. "Ah, Anglais!" he welcomed.

"Bonjour!" I replied, cutting his expected rhetoric with... "Where are the bikes and Olive? Where is she?" My tone implied that I needed answers immediately.

Henri informed me that the bikes had been taken further away from the road, on the approach of the troops.

"Olive?" I enquired.

"Olive? She is safe." He gave exaggerated, imitation kisses, teasing, "Olive's up here!" With that, he began blowing kisses to me. Great fun. 'Onion Face' joined in, pointing at me and grinning; both having a good laugh at Olive and my concern for each other's safety. I immediately blew elaborate kisses into the air, which amused them greatly.

The three of us happily walked through the bushes and into a wooded area. Eventually, I saw Olive as we came into a clearing. She was having a group discussion, standing up. Someone suddenly pointed in my direction. Olive immediately turned and left the group, hurrying over to the three of us.

"Oliver, my God, you are safe!" A great hug followed.

After our initial, emotional meeting, I jokingly enquired, "Where's the coffee and croissants?"

I was amazed at her reply. "Not our usual coffee Oliver, and no croissants, only a good German coffee and German sausages!"

With my eyebrows raised, and my mouth opened to speak, she countered, "Don't ask Oliver, just don't ask!"

CHAPTER 13

We left the camp area and returned to the cottages on our bikes, without any problems. The gendarmerie was still active in the area and were pursuing their line of enquiry. They suspected that Paul must have had assistance to escape from the clutches of the murderer in the barn.

We were fortunate that the gendarmes had visited the cottages whilst we were away, but it was deemed unsafe to return to the barn.

Paul's wife insisted that I stayed with her and Paul. Their two children would stay at a cottage, further along the road, with their aunt and uncle. This was for obvious security reasons. Olive would stay at the café with Marie.

Paul's wife tried to persuade me, without success, to sleep in their bed and they would use the children's beds. I insisted that I would sleep on one of the children's beds; it would be no problem for me, because I could sleep anywhere, and be awake at the slightest foreign noise.

My first breakfast was, of course, croissants and a very nice hot coffee. I found out later that Olive had left Paul's wife some German coffee.

Both Paul and his wife were so eager to make me comfortable. However, when Paul was out working, or on duty, she became so attentive, talkative and close that it was quite embarrassing! She tried to convey to me through her French - and my understanding of the language - that she wanted to show her thanks, for saving her husband's life, as only a woman could do. I reassured her, very convincingly, but in a nice way, that it was not necessary. That it would be a betrayal to Paul. She accepted it, but still insisted that she had a prolonged hug!

Circumstances suddenly changed. Olive and Monsieur De Cautemps called at the house mid-morning of the third day. With his usual charm and calm demeanour, and exercising his good manners, he sat down. Olive took Paul's wife's arm, and both left the house.

As soon as they had cleared the house, he asked me how I was coping with my situation, and seemed to be intent on hearing what I had to say.

Eventually he reported, "Due to the local situation, including the barn murder, it is amazing and, might I say, very impressive that you have lasted this long. You were not expected to! This area situation was not envisaged. You are not a professional in the network, just a wartime temp. However, because you are still active, a very important task has been given to you; a type of mission which was originally expected for you to tackle.

"The core of the task is top secret and will only be known to you, and you alone. You will be required to go out to another area, approximately seventeen miles from here. Olive will be in charge of your travel arrangements and will liaise with another group. Olive will not know the actual mission. She will help you to get to the scene and hand you over to another group. Once your destination is reached, further instructions will be given to you. It will be tricky Oliver."

"When will I be going?" I asked, trying to digest this new information.

"Shortly. That is all I know. This visit is just to prepare you." After a short while, we shook hands and he left me.

Olive returned on her own and informed me, "Paul's wife is with her children at the other cottage." Raising her eyebrows and changing her tone, she continued. "Well, Oliver, things seem to be heating up for you now, don't they? Perhaps the invasion will happen soon. I am only in charge of your safety until you are handed over to the other group. I know quite a few of them, and they have always been reliable and friendly."

"Nothing else you can tell me?" I enquired, feeling that there was more.

"No!" she choked, "I don't want to know. I must not know. It is not a resistance matter. Knowledge can be such a dangerous thing to possess, and you won't know where you are going until you get there, in case you are captured." She was visibly upset, but left quietly.

After climbing on my little child's bed, later in the evening, I analysed the situation. 'Perhaps another agent had 'bought it' and I was a temporary replacement?' If that were to be the case, I hoped that it would not be a permanent move into a strange group. Here, I had so many good friends and allies. I now felt so confident in my own ability, especially boosted and happy; this seemed to be a definite order from London. I smiled to myself, remembering how I had felt on my first night in France. I had come a long way and 'grown up' a lot since then and in a comparatively short time. Yes, it was about time I was allowed to do something, be aggressive and show my true Aries sign.

Happier now, I slept soundly on my little bed.

CHAPTER 14

Olive arrived early next morning, before our usual mid-morning coffee. She swept in casually with, "It is on Oliver. Tonight. You are going tonight!"

"Mon Dieu! That's a bit sudden isn't it?" I replied, incredulously.

"It is all arranged. We will travel a couple of miles on our bikes, before it gets dark, to meet your new escort and guide." Olive regaled, sipping her coffee.

Later, after I had eaten my meal, I gave Paul's wife a hug. Paul came in to the cottage specially to say goodbye. He had tears in his eyes and hugged me more than his wife. So emotional, these French characters. We said our goodbyes, and I expressed my thanks to them. Paul and his wife left the cottage to return to work; his wife was going to see the children. I guessed to bring them back home, after I had left the cottage.

"What about food on the journey?" I enquired of Olive.

Teasingly, she responded, "You are not going on a picnic Oliver. You will be stopping en route, travelling only during darkness. Don't worry Mon Cher, you will be fed."

I gave an exaggerated sigh of thanks. Olive was always teasing me about my appetite. "You had better rest this afternoon. We will be leaving at 1700hrs."

I did rest, but didn't sleep. It wasn't in my routine to sleep in daylight.

At 1700hrs Olive entered the room, gave me my shoulder holster and automatic, reminding me, "Just in case Oliver." We left the cottage, on our bikes, turning on to the country road, travelling until we met two members of the new group.

After preliminary introductions were completed, Olive and I had a very intense hug, before reluctantly parting.

I was very surprised when one of my two new companions, named Richard, spoke to me in almost perfect English. He said, "I've never heard of anyone getting that close to Olive, she must think an awful lot of you. Most of the members think of her as a very cold fish."

I replied, "Yes, she can be. She has many faces. I am happy to be a close friend of hers." Changing the subject, I continued "You speak very good English Richard."

"Yes! Thank you" he politely responded. "I lived in England during my childhood, and learnt the language due to being in the company of English boys. My mother was French and my father was English. He died, unfortunately, a few years ago, so we returned to France, to be near mother's kinfolk. I must tell you that our companion, travelling with us, has no knowledge of English whatsoever, so you can speak freely. We will be riding on this little known track for quite some time until we reach a cottage, which will be about four o'clock. We will stay there for the remainder of the night, resting until breakfast. The occupier is a woman living there on her own, and is man mad. If you feel inclined, feel free!" He laughingly added, "It depends how desperate you are. Whether you do or don't, it will not alter the fact she will be cooking you a good breakfast. She was married to a Welshman, for many years, who just loved a good breakfast. No croissants for him!"

As we cautiously rode onwards, I experienced a little bit of nostalgia. We had masked lights on our bikes, due to the blackout regulations. Akin to the lights I used to have on my bike when doing cycle patrols in the Home Guard. Just these little moments of nostalgia weaving through my mind. 'I would just love to be home once again.' Yes, such loving thoughts, to be immediately dismissed. Discipline had to prevail. 'You are not going home. You are going to God knows where, to do God knows what!'

After a few more miles, we heard Richard's companion, who was riding a little way ahead of us, shouting. We both drew our weapons, dismounted and walked cautiously towards what appeared to be a confrontation. One man was arguing with our companion. Richard hissed, "For goodness sake, it is a farmer who thinks we are burglars, attempting to steal his farm produce."

As we advanced nearer the scene, Richard suddenly called out greetings. Turning, he reassured me, "I know this man. It will be ok."

The farmer obviously recognised Richard by his voice, as he approached us, but seemed to make a sudden rush towards me! I brought my automatic up to protect myself as I did not know him, or his intentions. He stopped dead in his tracks crying out, "Mon Dieu, mon amie!"

Richard conversed in rapid French with the farmer. Patting me on the back, he confirmed, "It is ok Anglais, my idiot of a companion has told him that you are Anglais. He just wants to welcome you."

I replaced my automatic into its holster. The farmer resumed his advance towards me. I received a most friendly hug, and kisses on both cheeks, from what I can only imagine it would be like to be kissed by a hedgehog! He offered us hospitality, which was declined with our thanks. Richard chatted with him, emphasising not to divulge our meeting.

We continued pedalling into the night.

This episode did nothing to give me any great confidence in my new group. We eventually turned right, on to a farm track, and arrived at our destination; another farmhouse. It was quite some time before the door opened. The lady occupier showed herself, in the dim light from the cottage interior. She was smiling. I thought that even such a dim light showing in the UK would certainly ruffle the feathers of the local air raid warden, and bring forth a torrent of harsh words, Sergeant Major style!

We stowed our bikes out of sight, against the rear wall of the cottage. The three of us entered the property, closing the door behind us. I was introduced to Maria, who gave us a very warm welcome. She was a very cheerful little tubby woman; I should guess to be in her fifties. She showed us two rooms for us to rest in. Richard and I in one room, and the 'Frenchie' in the other one. We welcomed a quick invitation to retire, which we took advantage of. My first impression of Maria was that of a very pleasant, cuddly woman. This was my last thought as I dropped off to sleep.

We slept soundly until 0800 and washed in a small room, with water produced by a hand pump from the well.

The best was to come. A truly wonderful sight. A breakfast consisting of quite a large steak, accompanied by two fried eggs, mushrooms and toast! I had not seen such a meal for a long time. During my breakfast, I realised that the steak did not seem to taste like a beef steak and suspected that it was horse meat. Even so, it was a great breakfast experience.

I stayed close to Richard as much as I could. Any temptation to get close to Maria was terminated by her 'perfume', consisting of a combination of heavy garlic and a farmyard aroma! Our other companion must have liked this unusual combination because, during the day, he was shown around Maria's bedroom; closing the door to keep the perfume in.

Richard and I relaxed most of the day, discussing life in England. The three of us stayed until the early hours of the morning. Continuing on our journey so as to arrive at our destination just before dawn. Eventually, we stopped at a medium sized farm house. After passing through a gate, and stone yard, we accessed the house through the front door. It was Richard's sister's house.

She had an interest in horses, judging by the stables in the yard. Richard's sister was absent. He said that she had gone away for a time, because he did not want her to be involved in any resistance activities. A few farm hands maintained the health of the horses, and all the other aspects of the farm. They slept in billets attached to the farm buildings. They were, of course, devout members of the resistance group.

The interior of the farmhouse was very comfortably furnished. There was hot water on tap. A wonderful luxury. I treasured it and didn't waste a drop. I had a wonderfully comfortable feather bed, which teased out all the tensions from my body during the night. I felt absolutely magnificent on waking next morning.

The following evening, I received a visitor. A very serious individual, dressed in farmer's attire. He made sure that we were completely on our own before commencing the conversation. In a low voice, he almost whispered, "There is a Telephone Exchange in the town. Your task is to listen to a conversation at a certain time. When the conversation is finished, you must disconnect the line for a specific period, until you hear another call commence on another circuit. As soon as this call commences, you must disconnect it. Go to the other one and restore it to service, then wait five minutes to reconnect the other one. All traces of your presence must be obliterated. Can you cope with this technically?"

I assured him that I could do so providing I could gain access to the equipment.

"You will have assistance to gain access to the building. It is all the assistance that can be given."

"That is all I need. Once inside I will be able to cope." I confirmed.

My visitor continued, "The actual times will be given on the day, but I will give you the numbers now."

After he had given me the numbers he urged, "For God's sake, don't mix them up! The first number is the first call to work on. Remember them, then you must destroy them. I will visit you once again and you will repeat the numbers to me in the right sequence. I will return in two hours' time. You have two hours to list your requirements to enable you to carry out the work." He left as mysteriously as he had arrived.

It was all serious stuff. No preliminary nonsense. No welcome, "How are you?" and definitely no 'huggies'! He had a job to do and was doing it. Thank God they were only four figure numbers; not as they are now, of eleven each one. He did return, two hours later. I liked his style. Bang on time!

To pre-empt some of my questions, he reported, "You will be able to view the building beforehand and a locksmith will first go to the building to unlock the door. The staff will have left the building. It will be dark inside, but quite a lot of light may come in through the windows; it could well be a clear night. It will be in two days' time."

I had a list of requirements, which I gave to him. He surveyed them intently. He confirmed, "Yes, I will get these for you tomorrow at 1200 hrs. You will repeat the numbers, and your sequences, each time I visit you."

I spent the remaining time left, until 1200 hrs the next day, repeating the numbers in my mind. I was remembering which of the numbers to access, and the right order. Before I fell asleep, I repeated them over and over again; reminding myself of my childhood days, when I was learning how to spell.

The next morning, Richard and I went into the town on our bikes, stopping at a safe house in the town. We went in, and up the stairs, into a room overlooking the Telephone Exchange building. We looked through net curtains, first making sure that there was no light, or daylight, behind us. It was quite a busy road with mostly people wandering about. Then a shock! At the end of the building, on the left hand side, was a makeshift hut. This housed a German soldier, and a gendarme, sitting casually on chairs, with a small table between them. They looked very relaxed and bored. No one had mentioned the attendance of a guard!

After observing them for a while, I thought they were very lackadaisical; which made me more hopeful of the success of this operation. Occasionally, the gendarme twisted around in his seat and glanced a momentary glance alongside the front of the building, before returning to his original position.

I asked Richard what time they changed the guard. If I were to attempt an entry into the building, by the front door, during the evening, I would wish to observe the guard who would be on duty during that period. I did not think that Richard had been consulted, or given any details. He seemed very vague about some of the questions I put to him.

He answered my question rather nonchalantly, "I think it is about 1700-1730, but I'm not sure."

"Well! You don't think they change the guard? Don't you know?" I exclaimed.

He smoothed his chin whilst contemplating. I hurriedly continued my questioning. "Has anyone planned and done their homework for the operation? I was not told that there would be a military guard. I sincerely hope the locksmith is up to his job. Does he know that he has the guard to cope with? It is a waste of time watching the guard today. I must watch them prior to the time of the operation. The guards might have a different time and attitude. I must return to the farmhouse, I have an appointment at 1200 hrs." With that, I left.

Promptly, at 1200 hrs, I received my visitor who gave me: my pencil torch, beret, plimsolls (size 10.5) and telephone butt, which I had requested.

"Oh no! This telephone butt (a metal, telephone handset) has an equipment plug on the end. I requested that it must be modified to two wandering crocodile clips!" I blurted out.

"It couldn't be done in the time." My visitor apologised.

"It will have to be done. Bring me pliers, wire cutters and a small screwdriver and I will do the modification. It is essential for what I propose to do." I urged.

I think he was impressed with my attitude. "I will return with it modified or with the tools you have requested." He said. "The operation is at 1800 hrs tomorrow. I will return tomorrow at 1500 hrs, I will also have the connection times. I'm sorry, but the connection times will not be known until then."

I thought that this operation is getting worse as it goes on. It will only give me 3 hours to memorise, to get on site, possibly modify the butt, observe the guard and use my judgement.

At 1500 hrs my sombre visitor arrived. I couldn't believe it. He had a faint smile on his face as he handed me the modified telephone butt. "Voila! It is as you requested." One job less for me to do. My visitor gave me the times associated with the operation and for the last time asked me to repeat the numbers. He then held out his hand. "Good luck ole boy, you might well need it!" then smiled and went. He turned as he went through the door and waved. He had really had me fooled. He was English!! I just had to grin. Just brilliant!

I checked my 'kit': Butt, torch, beret, plimsolls. I wished to have a beret to conceal my hair in the possibility that I might need to change my appearance. The plimsolls for flight of feet if pursued, plus ease of movement once (if lucky) I was inside.

I kept repeating the first number with its time, then the second number. My head was also full of the possibilities, probabilities involved in the mission. I had only three hours to get there, observe the guard, if changed, watch for the locksmith to unlock the door (if lucky), and I would need to be twenty minutes inside for familiarisation of the place.

Richard and I sallied forth once again from the farmhouse, we had no problems getting there. Arriving at the house, we went upstairs once again to observe the Telephone Exchange building and the movement, if any, of the guard. I was getting a wee bit anxious now. The guard hadn't changed. It gave me almost no time to look around inside the building and to observe the new guard to see how often he checked the door and side of the building. I was observing the present guard in case the guard did not change.

Then thank the Lord, it suddenly happened; the soldier arrived in a truck, occupied by other soldiers. He dismounted just as the gendarme arrived on his bike. The four of them then decided to have a chat. 'For goodness sake, two of you go home.' It was getting perilously close to the time of the operation and the tension was mounting. Eventually, the four of them parted and the new guard settled in. The new gendarme was fatter than the previous one and it was quite some time before he decided to look around at the front door.

My latest target time approached. Where is the locksmith? It would all have to be cancelled if he did not appear, then Richard said, "There he is, walking down the road, his eyes no doubt watching the guard hut." When he arrived at the Telephone Exchange building he just casually turned off the pavement and went up to the front door, fiddled with the handle and the lock, turned around and left, continuing his walk up the road. I could not believe it; he could not possibly have 'fixed' the lock in so many seconds.

I turned to Richard expressing my concern. He shrugged his shoulders and said, "The locksmith is one of the best, in fact the best, but I do agree it did seem a bit too quick, because I think there are two locks."

"I will soon find out. I'm on my way now Richard."

We shook hands, and he reassured me, "I will be watching." I gave him a wry smile and went down the stairs and out on to the road; very concerned about how much time I had. I turned right and walked about 100 yards, crossed the road and came back on the other side. The Telephone Exchange was now on my right hand side and the guard hut at the far end of the building. As I approached, with my eyes fixed on the guard hut, the gendarme suddenly got up and stretched. I slowed my pace and hoped I would not have to repeat my walk. He looked over towards the door in my direction, obviously bored, then turned around and sat down. I felt so relieved. It was so very unlikely that he would become a problem now. A fleeting thought, 'thank God I wasn't 15 seconds earlier!'

I turned the handle of the door; it had a key lock underneath and a Yale type lock higher up the door. Hey presto! Easy, I just walked in. What a clever locksmith. He must have fixed both locks. How the devil could he have managed in a matter of seconds? I closed the door quietly behind me and thought how light it was, especially at the far end.

'Oh my God! There is someone in here!' At the same time, seeing the large key inside the lock, I moved down the aisle between the equipment racks and saw a man, probably an engineer, bent over, writing on a long desk with the aid of a table lamp. No wonder the locksmith was so quick. It wasn't locked. Thank God for my plimsolls. Good thinking Oliver. They made no noise on a hard wooden block floor, heavily waxed. I should have had 20 minutes at least to start my action. I now had exactly seven.

I soon discovered the layout. Surprising how much light from the table lamp but there was a problem, the place where I had to work was only about 10 feet from the individual at the desk. I stealthily crept up the aisle, worked my way along the racks towards him, until I came to my numbers. I put a piece of card by the second number, so that I could immediately see it without any hesitation, then I found my first number. I had four small cards to insulate the spring contacts at the right moment and, easily restoring the circuits by removing them, leaving no trace of my 'work', I then settled down, concentrating. I was listening to the conversation of the first number when the engineer got up and walked very close, one rack away from me, to check something, then returned to his desk. I had an action plan to deal with him, but it was not needed.

Time seemed to drag, waiting for each moment, but my mission went like clockwork, yes, exactly to plan. I was highly delighted and relieved. Mission accomplished! Easy now. All I had to do was walk out. Warily, I checked that I had all my 'kit' with me, nothing left to denote a visitation.

As I was pussy footing my way to the door, I heard, then saw it open. I swiftly moved down the equipment aisle and peered through the racks to see a woman in her late twenties, or early thirties, half inside the door, with her left hand on a pram which remained outside the door. I also noticed that the key was still on the inside door lock handle unit. As the door was pulled wider I noticed the gendarme. He said something to the woman which made her laugh. The woman suddenly shouted, resulting in the appearance of the engineer. He came to the door and started a conversation with both the woman and the gendarme. She held the engineer's hand and appeared to be enquiring about him coming home for their meal. I noticed the gendarme leave, but even so if the engineer left now I would be in trouble. He would release the Yale lock which would of course not be a problem, but he would certainly take the door key and lock it from the outside locking me in the building. Mmm! To say that I was beginning to be concerned about my safety would be an understatement.

They certainly took their time discussing some problem. I was looking at them through the equipment racks on my knees. They wouldn't see me, it would be similar to someone looking from some bushes or trees, especially so because it was also at a low height being on my knees. Eventually they came to a decision. I understood it to be that he would be coming home shortly.

She then moved after a fleeting kiss, pushing the pram with her left hand and pulling the door shut with her right hand. I gave her a couple of minutes then I crossed the aisle and quietly opened the door a couple of inches, looking through the gap with my left eye, in the direction of the guard hut. The woman was just leaving the guard and hut. When he sat down I slipped out of the door and on to the road. I had just crossed the road, retracing my route back to the house, when I saw two Citroen saloon cars arrive, screeching to a halt outside the Telephone Exchange building. Gendarmes were spilling out of them. And just as I was about to enter our safe house, a German camouflaged staff car arrived at the Telephone Exchange with two German officers. I met Richard, and confirmed, "I'm back, in spite of your group's abominable planning!" He gravely shook his head in agreement.

CHAPTER 15

Richard and I left the house so that the couple who owned it could possess it once again. We pedalled a few hundred yards to a vacant, small, 'safe' house in its own ground, complete with driveway, where we could stay until all the activity in the area had subsided.

We expected to stay approximately two weeks; the plan would be for us to cycle to Richard's sister's farm, with two scouts riding ahead of us as a precaution, in case check points had been set up. We hoped to be able to spend time at the farm, in idle luxury, to await instructions.

Richard dealt with food rations and shopping; I had to stay indoors in case someone recognised me and associated me with the exchange incident.

We had been there for ten days when I received a caller, whilst Richard was out of the house. He stood at the door, reassuring me in a very strong French accent, "It is ok Anglais, it is urgent that I must visit you here."

At first I was wary. I was more than ready to reach for my shoulder holster.

He came in, all smiles, with the usual courtesies, carrying quite a large canvas bag. I relaxed as he reiterated, "I know I am a stranger to you, but I have emergency instructions for you."

"You are no stranger, despite your heavy accent and with your new mode of dress and glasses. You are the same person I saw prior to undertaking a certain mission." I replied, smiling broadly.

"How come you think that?" he said, looking rather bewildered.

"You walked into the room the same way as when you walked in to see me a few days ago. Your face, all smiles, doesn't hide your basic dour expression, which you had then. Plus, the fact that your eyes are still blue, the same as mine. So you can cut out the 'Mondieus' and 'Bonjours' and speak the King's English ol' boy."

"Hmm..." he said, "You are the clever one. Pretty observant for such a young un', and amateur too."

"It pays to be so."

"Yes. It certainly does." This time, spoken with no trace of an accent, except for a 'Westminster' tinge. He continued, "I will come straight to the point, with the purpose of my visit. You are in danger here, and I have come to take you out before your companion returns."

"Leave without informing Richard?" I enquired, not sure what to make of it all.

"Your life could depend on it. Vital!" he insisted, looking at me rather gravely.

I thought of all the luxury going to waste on the farm. All that lovely hot water. "Are you sure that I have to go? And who the hell are you anyway? I know that you are English and speak with a well-educated accent but..."

He broke in, "I have a permanent position, so to speak, and I call all the tunes. I am familiar with Monsieur De Cautemps and your mentor Olive. I will be instrumental in returning you into her care, unless I receive instructions to the contrary. I have clothes for you to change into. You must collect everything belonging to you." He was quite insistent.

"What danger can there be here for goodness sake? I'm in a nice safe house!"

"You are only an infinitesimal part, in a very large wheel, and I am a much larger part, knowing much more than you do.

It is my profession. I know, for instance, that the engineer at the exchange has been arrested and taken for interrogation. Nobody should be aware, or have any knowledge of, your last mission, except Richard, but this group appears to have a leak in it. It is now known that an Anglais was responsible for the sabotage at the exchange. They are 'on to you' Oliver. They know who you are and where you are. They don't want the French engineer to be blamed for the sabotage, and suffer the consequences, especially by an Anglais who has already knifed and killed a French man!"

I rebuked that statement with amazement, "I did not kill anyone!"

"I know that." he said, "things get so distorted amongst the 'Frenchies'. Richard will be purposefully delayed until we leave these premises, but even so, we will go now. You will come with me. You must not trust Richard, or anyone connected with this group."

I changed into a jacket and trousers and left the house with my new companion, walking down the drive, carrying my bag of clothes. "Aren't we going to use the bike?" I enquired.

"No monsieur. Leave it where it is. I have a car waiting."

"What do I call you? What code name do you have?" I asked. Clearly, I couldn't call him nothing.

"You don't call me anything!" he snapped back at me.

"For God's sake, I can't just call you…"

Interrupting - he was very good at that - he casually quipped, "Call me what you like. Call me Joe if that makes you happy."

"OK." I said, "Hello Joe, what d'ya know?"

He grinned at that.

As we walked down the path, and turned left on to the road, three shots rang out in rapid succession. I immediately drew my hand gun and dropped down on one knee to present a smaller target. As I did so, a gendarme slowly crumpled to the floor, from behind some bushes across the road. His hand gun following suit, clattering on to the ground. There was a shout from a car parked further up the road on our left, and on the same side as us. "Quick!" urged Joe, "Into that car!" So we did.

As we sped off, the driver said, "That gendarme was waiting with his gun in his hand, albeit for you Oliver." He seemed genuinely concerned for me.

"I don't think he would have shot you. It was mostly to keep you there until you were captured. I did say that they were on to you. Not all the gendarmes are pro-resistance." Joe responded.

"Yes, I do accept that, but the majority are our friendly De Gaulle types. Others are anti-British characters, especially after we sank their navy with such a loss of life. And of course, there are the followers of Marshal Petain who do not wish to upset the Germans, not forgetting the real diehard 'commies'." I added.

"Yes, got it all in one sentence. Let us hope German intelligence is not included." Joe agreed.

Then, changing direction, he asked, "What the hell made you get involved in murderous French squabbles? It has made life difficult for all concerned. This is one example. They talk too much and get it all wrong, so coming to the wrong conclusion. Their vendettas carry on from generation to generation. Things could be very difficult for you, especially now in France, but also later if you do get back to England, both for you and your family."

"I could not just stand by and see my resistance friend killed. Even with hindsight, I would still have done the same." I insisted.

"Hmmm... tricky!"

"Ever so!" I replied.

A few more minutes and we pulled up at a two storey house, with a brass knocker on the door. Before Joe could insert his key in the door it was opened, from the inside, by a fair haired female. Joe turned around and waved to the driver, as the car pulled away from the house.

"Margaret, Oliver!" introduced Joe, tersely.

Margaret smiled and welcomed me, "Greetings Oliver."

"Ditto, Margaret." I received a big smile for that.

"So, you are Oliver. You look so young, I know Olive very well and she has told me a lot about you, but I still did not expect you to look so young!" Margaret noted, as she cast her eye over me.

I weighed Margaret up: Older and taller than Olive; darkish, mostly concealed by a fair blonde colouring. She had wide awake brown eyes, blue 'satin type' blouse and a lovely shaped chest. Yes, a nice looking woman in her late thirties or early forties. She was straight and outspoken, Yes, I liked her very much in the short time I had known her. I guessed that she was British.

Eventually we sat down. Margaret began telling me, "I have worked with Joe for many years, and he seems impressed with you. He has brought you here so that you will be out of harm's way but, it is only because you may be useful to the cause that you are here. I know, I've been down that road. It's not because they love you Oliver.

"Everything is much more sophisticated here. It's a pity your French is so diabolical, otherwise perhaps you could be here permanently. Olive has had me in stitches laughing about incidents concerning your French." Margaret finished, smiling at me.

I smiled with her, thinking of some of the incidents concerning my French, but the thought of being on the permanent staff. 'Oh no! Not for me. Not a way of life for me. Definitely not my cup of tea!'

I settled in quickly at my new abode. There was very little in the way of furniture, but meals were at a table with knives and forks. There was veggie food, bubble and squeak and pigeon, which I had never had in England. There was porridge, with no sugar at first, which I thought was ghastly as salt was used instead. Margaret said that it was because sugar was very scarce and the Scots ate it that way. Being an absolute gem of a woman, she found someone who had beehives, so I was able to have honey, and sometimes honeycombs, in my porridge. It was all such a change from pastry based meals.

Joe was absent most of the time I was there. Odd people would drift in and out, but there was no mingling, no introductions. All the time, in the back of my mind, was that everything seemed geared for a quick departure if it had to be. Nothing was left lying around and, as I said previously, there was little in the way of furniture.

One morning, Margaret apologised, 'I'm sorry that you are in limbo Oliver. Olive told me that you hate inactivity, but it has to be. She also told me to look after you whilst..." she stopped in mid-sentence, as Joe came in, suddenly interrupting. He seemed to have a passion for that!

"I'm sure Margaret has filled you full of information and is keeping you well fed. She is good at both. Contrary to what Margaret has hinted at, there is no way that you could possibly be permanent, even as a student. You need vast experience and perfect French!" Grinning as he completed the sentence.

I was elated to hear that.

He continued, "A new project is being envisaged, which will mean travelling well out of the area covered by your pass.

96

The feasibility is being studied. We must be prepared in case it gets the go ahead. I will take your Latvian pass and secure it. You will have a new pass and a new set of papers. Most probably you will not need them, but it is just in case. We will be going by rail. The story is that you will be partly deaf with a speech impediment." He couldn't resist grinning as he continued "The part is made for you. It will suit you because you can only comprehend French with great difficulty, so I suggest that you don't even try!" Then laughing, said, "Your speech impediment will cover your 'special French', known only to you Oliver. Another lady who should be here today or tomorrow, will be your aunt who will be able to communicate with you better than anyone else. You will stay together a lot so that you will look to have a proper relationship. The sustenance you are receiving here has not yet worked through to you, so you will still be able to look a bit pathetic, being still slightly undernourished. I will be around, but not with you on the journey. If the project starts looking a positive reality, we will stay nearer the site."

With this information in mind, I made my way back to my room. Margaret never did finish her sentence.

CHAPTER 16

My pseudo aunt did not arrive that day. It was late morning the next day when she arrived. Her name was also Margaret; fortunately, she had a second name, Louise, which was not normally used. It was decided we would use the name 'Louise', to avoid confusion with our resident Margaret.

Louise had a jovial disposition, with an easy smile. As I reciprocated her smile, I thought, 'yes, you will be a great aunt Louise.' She spoke English and I learnt, through eaves dropping, that she had French and English parents. Louise looked like an auntie; somewhat older and smaller than myself, with slightly chubby cheeks and dressed for comfort.

We sat down on the settee and I addressed her, "Nice to meet you Louise."

"Naughty boy! I am now your auntie and don't you forget it." She scolded, but with a twinkle in her eye.

"Yes, auntie!" I chirped, matching her twinkly eyes with mine.

We immediately started an important routine. I spoke in my French, only if absolutely necessary. Auntie did the talking. We had our meals together; separated from anybody else. She spoke to me only in French, slowly so that I could comprehend. Perfect for me, and ideal to portray our relationship of an aunt and slightly backward nephew.

She filled me in with a background: My parents were killed; no sisters or brothers; the house description where I used to live; various friends and two uncles that I had once known; foods I liked and my favourite foods. I liked swimming under supervision, plus idiosyncrasies associated with me. Although it was serious business, probably never to be used but insisted upon by Joe, it was also fun. It had to be to make our relationship natural. All this just in case. Always, just in case!

After a fortnight of this relationship, I became almost convinced that Louise was my aunt. I even believed that my French had improved!

One morning, Joe came in to tell us that we would be leaving the next day. I listened to what he had to say, then told him I needed to have details of what to expect, plus details, or at least an outline, of what I was expected to do. He stared at me. It was a stare he used to unnerve people, or to make them uncomfortable, to soften them up so that he could dictate the proceedings. Unfortunately, it did not work with me. I had found him out once and I think he knew it. He tried it just the same.

"You know I can't tell you that Oliver. Surely you know that?"

I persisted, "Do you know something? If you do know something, please tell me what you know. I don't like working in the dark. I have a right to know. Not the actual details, I just want to know the strategy, so that I can be prepared. I also need to protect myself, just as I have done up to now. Nearer the time of my actual mission, I will need to know every detail. I'm like an alley cat and will fight like one if needs be!"

He had a somewhat resigned look on his face. "I half expected this. Come into the other room. Excuse us ladies whilst we confer." When we were alone he continued quietly, "I don't want too many people full of information. It is dangerous!" With that, he glanced around the room, despite it being empty, other than us.

I enquired, "For whom? I am not many people."

"It is dangerous for the operation!"

"Aha!" I said, "If I don't know, there won't be an operation, and if you are detained, there will be no operation either."

Joe stared at me, then a smile slowly crept across his face. Reluctantly, he conceded, "You impressed me, the first time we met, with your eye for detail and your requests. You could be right in this instance. I will give you an outline of what I know to date. This is our first phase, with reference to travelling. You and your aunt (I noticed that he didn't refer to her as Louise.) will have rail tickets, but you will alight two stations before your ticket destination. I will travel separately, to the next station. You will be met and taken to a house. I will join you from a different direction later. We will then await further instructions, which we will both work on as there will be security and entry issues to discuss, and technical tasks for you to peruse."

Margaret poked her head around the door and told Joe he had a message. "Ok." he acknowledged, and left the room.

Two minutes later he returned. "The operation has been postponed until the day after tomorrow."

During the following day, we found that the train did not stop at the station from which I was going to alight. I suppose wartime schedules were unreliable. Other arrangements had to be made, which occupied Joe most of the day. Eventually, it was decided that we could all now disembark at the same station.

We used a local bus to get to the nearest railway station; auntie and myself travelling separately from Joe. There was hardly anyone on the platform when a massive black French locomotive, pulling the coaches and hissing steam, arrived. To me, it looked so powerful; likened to a great black stallion. I was pursuing this liberty of thought, with my usual wry sense of humour, when I was taken completely by surprise by a very weak, feminine, high pitched whistle emitting from the beast! To me, its character suddenly changed. No longer was it a black stallion, it was now a huge buxom lady. I smiled inwardly, a few seconds of childlike thinking, then immediately back to reality.

There were two German soldiers in the compartment; one trying to sleep with his head cupped by his hand against the window, and the other one struggling to read a paperback. After we had been travelling awhile, I noticed that the soldier in the corner was not actually sleeping, his eyes were minutely opening to a narrow slit observing me. I wasn't fazed. I just kept a 'travel bored' expression on my face. However, I can imagine that it could quite easily induce 'give away' symptoms in anyone 'on the run', feeling nervous and apprehensive.

Suddenly, whilst I was imagining such a situation, the door opened to reveal a ticket inspector. He was standing next to a civilian. He had a thin grey face in contrast to the ticket collector's face; big boned, chubby red cheeks and bushy eyebrows. The inspector asked auntie for her ticket. The civilian asked to see her pass. I was then asked for my ticket and pass. I was starting to get just a little apprehensive as he scrutinised my pass for quite some time. Even more so when it was requested that I should step out of the compartment into the company of a German soldier, who had a complete non-committal expression on his face.

I was not a happy bunny at this turn of events. A little while later, both the inspector and the civilian came out of the compartment. Looking at me with an obvious false compassionate face, the civilian drawled, "I am sorry that your mother is so sick. Your aunt says that it is upsetting you so much."

With an obvious confused expression, I questioned, "My aunt said that?"

"Yes." answered the civilian. "Still, it is good that your father is so well."

I knew the game plan, I could quite easily have agreed with him, having no other option, if we had not invented a background. I shook my head, "You must have misunderstood her sir." My heart was now pounding away in my chest.

"No." he confirmed. "That is what she said."

"It cannot be so; she was at my mother's funeral. My father is also dead. They were both killed!" I replied, forcibly.

He gestured, "Stay there whilst I speak to her again."

While he was gone, the French ticket collector smiled briefly before the civilian returned. "My apologies…" he said, "it is a misunderstanding of your language. I am German you see. Please return to your seat."

"Danke!" I replied, which brought forth a faint, cold smile.

He was most probably a gestapo minor employee doing a train routine. I sat down next to auntie, pretending to be a little confused about the incident. The German soldier in the corner had now changed his position, sitting properly in his seat. He had most probably taken a keen interest in the proceedings. He now smiled at both auntie and myself. Both the soldiers passed a few words to each other and laughed.

My respect for Joe and his methods certainly increased after the incident. 'Just in case. Yes, Joe, just in case!'

The journey was without any further incident. We went by car, from the station, to a building nearby, which turned out to be a block of flats. The driver took us up to a flat and gave us a key. Then he turned and, with a confident, friendly smile to both of us, squeezed my arm and left.

Once inside, I observed that it was another sparsely furnished place; a getaway flat, just enough comfort to make it tolerable. Aunt Louise gave it a frown, then a resigned slump of the shoulders.

"Très bon!?" I offered, laughing.

"If you say so garçon." replied auntie, opening and closing cupboards in her reconnaissance routine.

I could make out eggs, porridge, bread and clothing, during the brief periods of opening and closing the cupboards.

Auntie waited until Joe arrived before she organised refreshment. He would be having meals and socialising with us, but would spend the night and periods of the day in the next door flat.

I think it was a couple of days later when he came in and told me, "Ok Oliver, we move tomorrow." He produced a railway ticket for Aunt Louise and said, "You will leave later than our departure Louise, which will give you time to do the usual 'vacating routine' in the flat."

She nodded her head, evidently used to the procedure.

The next morning, after a shower, we had a change of clothing. I was now no longer the slightly backward nephew, I was back being the real Oliver once again. Auntie and I had a fond farewell, just prior to our departure. She whispered into my ear, "May God be with you." and as we parted, she crossed herself discreetly.

Joe and I came out of the flat and joined the morning traffic, on our newly acquired bikes. We travelled a few miles into town and turned left, across the road, into a side road. A few more turnings later, we arrived at a town cottage. We took our bikes around the cottage and locked them into a small shed at the rear. We then entered the cottage through the rear door.

Once we were settled, Joe took out some papers and asked me for my recent identity papers, which he took from me and burnt in the grate. He then handed me my original pass, plus a ration card.

I felt much happier now that I had returned to my original self; much more assured. I was also more confident that Joe was instrumental in the organisation of the operation, not like the previous shambles.

Next day, Joe received details of the task which lay ahead. We both sat down and studied the information.

I was to completely disconnect five numbers during the following evening, when there was no staff present, inside the telephone exchange building. I would have to wait until there was reduced traffic and few pedestrians outside, yet enough to allow me to mingle, and not be conspicuous.

The disconnections were to be done in such a way as to delay reconnection as long as possible. It was also stressed that I 'must' be out of the building within ten minutes of my first disconnection, to avoid capture.

Looking at the photographs, there were two doors to the building; the main entrance and another smaller door, which sunk into the wall of the building towards the far end. Both doors faced the road. It was this smaller door that I was to enter the building, with a key provided. The building was longer and bigger than the previous one, meaning that there would be more than one room; taking longer for me to find my way around once inside. There were no details available in reference to the internal lay out.

Joe asked, "Can you cope with this Oliver?"

Confidently, I replied, "If I have the time inside to make it possible, yes. I will need time to negotiate and find the equipment. It will be the M.D.F. once again, - the Main Distribution Frame. It is the only place where the circuits are within reach of each other. It is the only viable place. I will need all of the ten minutes to achieve what I have in mind. The limited time is what will be the biggest risk, along with the entry of course. If somebody is observing the building, and I

104

am observed entering, it will be curtains for me. If I should leave late, it could also be curtains! Technically, this will be straight forward, even though I intend to disconnect each circuit at more than one location. I do realise that after the first disconnection I must complete the other four and get out within ten minutes. That, I think Joe will be the tricky bit! Still, I won't be lumbered with a telephone butt. All I will need will be: wire cutters, a small piece of wire, a torch and to be wearing plimsolls. I will not have the added stress of a locksmith operating. Once in possession of the equipment I will be ready to go." I gave Joe a reassuring look.

"Good man!" congratulated Joe. "The getaway should be easy. Turn left on to the road, walk a few paces to a waiting car. The front door, passenger door, will not be fully closed. Jump in and meet me here. If the car is not there, just keep walking until you are picked up."

The next day, after sampling Joe's cooking, we both walked out into the early evening. I followed many paces behind. There were still quite a lot of people about, and I noticed much damage to property. We walked until I recognised the building. Joe walked on, passed the building, and I turned right into a small paved area, unlocked the door and walked into darkness.

All the windows were blacked out. I stood still for a few moments then, using my torch, I carefully moved forward through passage ways of empty and half-filled crates and boxes. Flashing my torch, it looked as though equipment was being installed. On reflection, I think it may have been 12 channel carrier equipment.

I went further forward - it was so damned dark and eerie - until I came to a door in a dividing wall. 'My God! What if it is locked?' Relief, as I noticed that there was no lock equipment, just a handle. I opened it and walked into the next room. Waving my torch around, firstly I noticed the test desk and then the M.D.F... 'Thank God for that, familiar territory.' I located and traced my numbers, stopping only to calm, and slow down, my heart a little; generally, to compose myself. I rehearsed the operation, looking at each number in turn, confirming the sequence that I wished to do. Operating in the right sequence would save valuable seconds. I went over it again in my mind because, once started, I would have to proceed efficiently to enable me to finish and get out within ten minutes.

Taking a deep breath, I reasoned that if I had been observed entering the building I would have company by now. This eased me a little; one stress removed. Nicely calmed and taking another deep breath, I started forcing springs out to disconnect them, but not so much as to be obvious. Cutting cross connections in the bed of wires. Some two, some springs once and others both, plus looping some together. I did not look at my watch, but just worked on methodically. I had programmed myself to do this and not waste seconds, until the rehearsed routine in my head was complete.

After what had seemed a long time, I finished the work. Flashing my torch on to my wrist watch, I noticed it had taken me twelve minutes. Quite a shock! I did not panic. I don't panic. I moved swiftly through the room, as fast as my torch would allow, through the inner door, then carefully, yet quickly, through the next room and its packing cases. With apprehension, I slowly opened the street door. A picture had evolved, in my mind, of a grey uniformed group waiting for me on the other side. I carefully peered into the street. No such group. I slid out, closed the door, locked it, and checked along the pavement. 'Glory be!' The car was there. I was into the car in a matter of seconds. The driver did not converse, just drove away normally. I did not look back. I was with Joe within five minutes.

Grabbing my shoulders with both of his hands, and staring into my eyes with a hopeful, yet joyous expression on his face Joe questioned, "You did it?"

"Yes!" I confirmed.

"Good man!" exclaimed Joe, slapping me on the back.

He poured two glasses of cognac. "I needed this Oliver and I am damned sure you do. A great success. Now you will have to get away out of the area quickly. I will try and get you back to Olive before all hell is let loose. They will be after you now Oliver, with a vengeance. You can be sure of that!"

With that, we both swigged back our cognacs.

CHAPTER 17

The whole situation was rather grave. My safety was at stake. Joe was quite clearly concerned for my welfare. "I have arranged a motorcycle and sidecar to take you rapidly away from here, before the Germans have realised what has happened and organise road checks. Once you have reached a distance of approximately twenty miles, you should be under Olive's influence; hopefully you will both meet up. Once you reach Olive, you will have a much better chance of staying alive."

With a smile, he continued, "I have some good news for you Oliver, which I am sure you will appreciate. The Allies have landed on the Normandy coast!"

"Normandy? Surely that must be just a diversion?" I asked, my mind barely taking it all in.

"No!" reassured Joe, "It is the real thing. All resistance groups have been receiving the long awaited radio codes, transmitted from the UK, to commence their attacks on selected targets. Your last completed mission was one of them. Damn good news to help you on your way! I know it is almost dark but, you must go now, at once. I really must reinforce what I said to you earlier, they are hopping mad and will be determined to hunt you down and get you. Your biker knows the roads, and the area, like the back of his hand. Even places where a road block would most likely be. He has many friends; knows the local people and farm buildings in the district. He is also a very brave and reliable man..."

Joe was just finishing giving me the 'frighteners' when Louis walked into the room. A nice looking mature man, from what I could see under his helmet and goggles, all dressed and ready. He spoke a certain amount of English; much better I think than my French was to him. He smiled broadly when I uttered a few French words. It did cross my mind that 'post war', I could quite easily become a French comic on stage!

Louis started issuing instructions, "There is no need to hold up the proceedings looking for extra clothing, let us go quickly; the sidecar has blankets and a windshield."

Respecting his advice, I passed good wishes to Louise and Margaret via Joe, as we quickly parted company.

With a firm, long handshake Joe urged, "Remember what I said, be aware. Be very aware! Especially if you think that you have got away with it. Still be on the alert. Goodbye Oliver and good luck!"

Just before boarding the bike, Louis warned, "I might have to stop suddenly at any time; I have friends along the route who will come out onto the road to warn us if they hear military movements, and possibly road blocks being set up. I thought you might like to know that."

"Thanks Louis." I replied, "It does wonders for my confidence."

I managed to munch two sandwiches, made up with some sort of 'bully beef,' as we wandered off to our means of transport; finishing the last part before climbing into the sidecar.

When I sat down, I felt as though I was sitting on the ground! With the blanket wrapped around and tucked into my bottom half, away we went. The town quickly went astern. It had been quite a busy thoroughfare, until we turned off after approximately five miles, on to a minor road. Every minute that passed, I felt that I was getting away with it. If I could only make it back to Olive and the barn, it would be so wonderful.

Suddenly, we came to an abrupt halt as a figure in the road waved us down. The trouble with masked headlights was that they did not show anything until the last moment. There was a short French discussion and we turned off on to an even smaller road - possibly a farm track - then stopped at a farmhouse.

"Stay here!" ordered Louis, marching up to the farmhouse door.

I felt like a visiting auntie, all wrapped up in the sidecar. The door opened but Louis did not go inside. On returning, Louis said that the occupiers had two young children. If the Germans visited and questioned them, they would soon find out through questioning the children; through childlike naivety, they would betray their parents. It was better not to go inside.

We went past the farm and further along the narrow track, turned left on to another lane.

After a short distance, Louis suddenly came to a halt and switched off the engine. "The sound of the motorbike will make us more vulnerable." He whispered.

I definitely agreed. It was so unearthly quiet.

I struggled out of the sidecar, feeling a little leg stiff. Just as we were about to push the bike to the next cottage, Louis informed me, "The cottage will be vacant. The owner was a bachelor and was killed in action. I know that there must be a couple of push bikes in the shed, so we should be ok as long as we are careful."

Then suddenly voices rang out, "Halt!" Light from torches blinded us. The sudden shock thumped my heart and filled me with utter dread. Just as I was beginning to think that I was ok. Joes' last words rang in my ears, 'Be aware, be very aware, especially if you think that you have got away with it!'. I immediately thought of Louis. What will happen to him? I knew what my fate would be, but poor old Louis. No chance to make a run for it; there were too many of them, and I was blinded by the light in my eyes.

Then a voice rang out "Louis? Louis?" Then another, repeating the same. As I accustomed my eyes to the immediate area, with the torches lowered, I realised that we were being threatened with an array of sten guns. British forces? Surely not. Then more voices shouting "Louis!?" then, "Anglais!" Unbelievable! 'Frenchies? My resistance friends?'

Then it started. A torrential downpour of rapid French between Louis and the Frenchies, intermingled with, "Anglais, we have been sent to look for you, Olive sent us."

"We thought you were a German patrol!" All the individual messages. "There are now road blocks on the roads which you have travelled on."

The relief I felt listening to the 'Frenchies' voices has to be experienced to realise its depth. They were enlightening me with news which I could hardly take in. I was still in a state of shock and a slow sense of recovery. I had almost accepted that the worst possible moment had arrived. It took a little while to absorb what was being said to me.

There were many willing hands available to push the bike and sidecar up to the cottage. On entering, it was full of Frenchies, dimly lit up by oil lamps. A great scene of happiness and excitement. Amongst them was Paul. He had insisted, with Olive, that he joined the others to come and look for me. It was a great reunion. He was such a genuine, emotional character and always jovial. We shared the same type of humour; our 'language trading' French and English could be hilarious.

Pointing to the stens I said, "You must have had a fruitful delivery." "Oui! Yes…" said Paul, "they came, just in time, a few days ago, one of them is faulty and cannot be used."

"Give it to me." I said, confidently. Within a minute I had 'sorted' the mechanism. "Any problems, pass them to me."

He was surprised that I could fix the 'stens'; turning around and telling the others.

Eventually, it was decided that we should rest the night inside the cottage. The 'Frenchies' would be outside, patrolling the area. They were all fired up now that the invasion had started.

Having such great confidence in my French friends, feeling sleepy and very emotional, I soon went away to sleep with the fairies.

I was in the middle of a wonderful dream when, "Anglais! Anglais!" ripped through my head. I was instantly awake. A Frenchie was bending towards me. "Anglais, it is dawn and a German patrol is nearby!"

The words which escaped my lips will not be repeated here. I had been suddenly torn from a wonderful, deserved, sleep into yet another adrenalin draining, ongoing situation. I heard the sound of machine gun and rifle fire before I left the cottage. The 'Frenchies' were firing from the cover of a hedge, and grass bank, with their feet in the ditch; making their weapons almost level with the grass field, on the other side of the hedge. I was told that one of them had been killed and another injured before they had time to find cover. However, they had inflicted casualties on the Germans, who were not far away, just on the other side of the field.

Paul ordered, "Come Anglais, we must go quickly on our way to the barn. We'll get breakfast when we get there. We can use bikes, it shouldn't take us long. Please Anglais, it is not your battle. It is not your country!"

He must have noticed my reluctance to leave. Assertively, I asked "Paul, did you recover the 'sten' from the Frenchie who was killed?"

"Yes" he said, "it is near the haversack."

I quickly went over to it and checked that the magazine held ammunition. On my way there, I saw an injured 'Frenchie' being transported by Louis, in the sidecar.

On returning, I insisted, "I am staying here to fight. I am taking his place!"

I was feeling so angry and upset. I wished vengeance on whoever had so abruptly ended my dream. I had had enough of escaping.

Paul remonstrated and another 'Frenchie' shouted at me, "Olive said we had to bring you back. You know too much! Come Anglais!"

"No!" I was adamant.

It was about time I had a go at them. Every sense dug in. Everything had boiled over. I was angry, and I am not an angry person. It took all my good judgement, and my sane self, to stop running across the field and having a go at them with my sten, but common sense prevailed.

Everything soon subsided. I became calmer once more. I swiftly went over to the hedge and joined the others. Once there, and in position, I felt happy in my new role, so much that I looked sideways and grinned at the 'Frenchie' next to me, who immediately raised his eyebrows. This is more like it. I was now more relaxed, firing at movement across the field. It was a great feeling fighting back.

After a period of exchanging fire, I noticed that the enemy was retreating close to the edge of the field, alongside the road which we had been on. One of them supporting a colleague, who had his arm around his neck. Another was being half carried; obviously a leg damaged. They were escaping alongside the hedge to provide cover, with their backs bent as much as possible to make a smaller target. I lowered my weapon. It was a German patrol not a large unit. The 'Frenchies' carried on firing.

I stood up and shouted "Halte! Halte!" to them. The thought of shooting anyone in the back, or a defenceless person, to me was unthinkable. Maybe battle hardened for a long time may make a difference? I don't know that it would. The 'Frenchies' stopped, and looked around at me.

"C'est le Boche! C'est le Boche!" they shouted, as though that excused it.

"But not in the back!" I replied.

The 'Boche' - the Germans - had now gone. I thought 'Good! Very good!' That was part 'payback time' for all the adrenalin that I had lost.

The 'Frenchies' were now laughing. I supposed it was relief they had won the day, but some were putting a finger to their temples and shouting, 'Boche'. I didn't care. I had my principles. I just joined and laughed with them. It was all great fun. I felt exhilarated, even though I had not had any breakfast. Not even a cup of coffee!

CHAPTER 18

When I returned from the hedge, I handed the sten gun to Paul. He didn't say anything, but I noticed he was giving me quizzical looks; having witnessed the change in my character.

After a short time in discussion, Paul, myself and two others, left the scene, on our bikes, and headed for the barn. After quite a few miles, and nearer to the town area, we stopped and decided to ride in separately, so that I would not be associated with them. 'Just in case'.

I was hoping that there would be no check point on entering the town. Check points were not mounted every day. 'If it was in operation' I thought, 'would it be just the normal garrison procedure, or a special one designed to filter out anyone who had not got a one hundred percent clearance?' Normally, any slight imperfection would be allowed through - it was information that I had gleaned from the gendarmes. If it was a special check to net and catch me, I could well be in deep trouble if my pass - although previously passed by a gestapo official in the square - was questioned.

My pass, handed back to me by Joe, had not been completely valid until I was back here in the area. Whilst I had been travelling, after leaving Joe, I had felt very vulnerable. I was somewhat out of my area and would have had to explain why. If just a routine check, most probably I could well get away with it, but not if it was a special check. It all depended on whether it was worth having to get a Latvian interpreter from somewhere. I think it was very shrewd of London to give me a Latvian identity. Yes, I had felt very vulnerable, except when I was with Aunt Louise; I had another pass to cover that area, and the travelling.

When I parted from Joe, he suggested that I leave my automatic with him. I did so very reluctantly. I felt that I needed its company for self-reassurance, but did agree with him. If it was found in my possession, at a check point, I wouldn't stand a chance. After Paul and co. had departed, I removed my black beret from my head and reverted to my original appearance in the local community. It was a calculated risk which I had had to take. Since leaving Joe, I had worn my black beret to minimise any association with my mission.

I rode the last few miles on my own and, coming around a corner, just before entering the built up area, I slowed down, with a certain amount of foreboding. There was a small queue, whose passes were being inspected. Three unfortunates were standing separately, with two armed soldiers.

I removed the pass from my pocket. When it was my turn I had to wait until the sergeant had scrutinised the pass of the person in front. 'Well this is it. Will I pass or not? Will it be scrutinised? Is it just a routine check?' Questions were bouncing around in my head.

I gave the pass to the soldier next to the sergeant, as well as putting on my well-rehearsed friendly smile. 'They were my friends!' As the soldier glanced at it, the sergeant turned around and looked at me. His face broke into a smile. He took the pass from the soldier and, without even looking at it, handed it back to me. I realised that it was the sergeant who had examined my pass previously in the square. His smile enlarged as he patted me on my shoulder and said something in German. I just replied "Danka." Accompanied, once again, by my well-rehearsed smile.

I remounted my bike. What a piece of luck that it was him, otherwise I might easily have been in trouble. I couldn't help thinking how very lucky I had been. 'Surely it will run out eventually? Sometime!'

I rode on in the direction of the barn, with the railway and the river on my right hand side; passing the wooded railings, where I had a close encounter with Olive. I was feeling so relieved and invigorated.

On the last road to the barn, I turned right into the cottages road and carried on until I reached the last cottage on the right, where there was war damage; replicating what I had done on a previous occasion, staying behind the wall of the last cottage for a good five minutes, before venturing out to detect if there had been any followers. Not a soul! I rode back the way I had come, to the end of the cottages road, sensing and seeing faces in the cottage windows.

When I arrived at the barn, Paul was there, ready to meet me and take possession of my bike.

We strolled past the ablutions, on the left, and into the barn. Making our way through the scattering of straw, I noticed quite a few strangers. It was about half way up the barn when I saw 'Onion Face'. He came down the barn to meet me, with a very happy face. He looked even bigger and scruffier than before; which I didn't think was possible! He engulfed me with his huge frame, enclosed in a long heavy coat. I had to endure his onion, garlic, B.O. fragrance for such a long time - well it seemed a long time - and being kissed on both cheeks. Paul thought it was hilarious. 'Onion Face' was so genuinely pleased to see me. He always was. Possibly, I was the only one to accept his friendship at close quarters. All the others, although loving this great character, showed it from a distance!

We reached the alcove and, looking at the thick straw on the floor, it was just like coming home. I recalled Joe's words, 'Once you get to Olive, you will have a much better chance of staying alive'. 'Well, I've done it, I'm back!' I just wanted to lie in the straw and take full advantage of the moment.

I said to Paul, "Go to your wife. Show her that you have returned!"

He laughed, "She will know, or will have assumed, that I have returned. The villagers in the cottages will have seen you. They don't miss anything! However, I will go now. You have a rest on your straw. I should expect Olive will be returning shortly."

I sat down on the straw, then stretched out on it to take full advantage of the occasion.

I slowly opened my eyes, taking in the scenery. When waking naturally, I never moved my head until I had taken stock of the area. 'Yes, I'm back!'

Olive was sitting nearby on the straw, looking at some papers. She glanced up. "Welcome Oliver!" and laughing said, "Where the hell have you been?" We had a hug full reunion.

Olive started to tell me what changes had taken place, then stopped abruptly, saying, "Here is a thermos of coffee and a bacon sandwich. I met Paul on my way back to the barn and he told me that you had missed breakfast and your beloved coffee. It is all I could manage to get you, but Paul is arranging a better meal as soon as possible." Grinning, she continued, "This is just to stop you from getting irritable!"

I had missed her humour. Yes, just one of the things I had missed. She continued talking, saying how things had changed during my absence.

"There are more new faces joining the resistance. Yes, more new faces Oliver, 'jumping off the fence' now that the invasion has started. I am not trusting any of them, until I have sorted and vetted them!"

'Yes,' I thought, 'You are well able to do that.'

"In the meantime..." she said, "we must still be very watchful; especially these new characters!" She then paused, with an expression on her face which I had seen before – something, or a subject, she found hard to express.

"What is it Olive?" I asked, trying to ascertain the reason for this look.

She smiled, recognising the fact that I knew she had a problem. "It concerns you." she said.

"Go on Olive, I can take it. Am I travelling once more?"

Then eye to eye, with a blank expression, she almost whispered, "Yes Oliver, you are going home. You have completed your work here. All we have to do is to get you back, when we are given the green light to do so." Her face was stony. She was hiding her emotion. I knew it.

I couldn't believe it. "Completed my work? Surely there is a lot more that I can still do?" I retorted, incredulously.

"No doubt there could be, my dear Oliver." (I could now see that she felt she was over the high hurdle) "That is not why you are here. You know why you are here, it is as I told you here in the barn, that your primary function will be communication sabotage, involving selected targets which will be given to you prior to the Allied invasion. You are not needed anymore Oliver. You have played your part. Although you have taken part, and been with us, you are not a member of the 'Resistance'. It is time to go home Oliver. Besides, the nights are warmer now. I don't need my hot water bottles anymore!"

That last remark made me smile. Olive continued, "When it was really cold, I stayed with Marie."

"Fickle woman!" I joked.

Olive then became quite serious once again. "Although you are among friends, you have also managed to acquire enemies. The Germans have agents searching for you, including many Frenchmen. There are the relatives of the character who died in the ablutions. They really believe that you killed him. Don't underestimate them Oliver. They are very much family orientated, and I can imagine that the gestapo is looking for

119

you in their own brutal, unpleasant, way and would dearly love to talk with you! So, for God's sake Oliver, be on your guard at all times. Be very aware. No one is invincible. Though sometimes, I think you are, but you are not!"

I replied to Olive saying, "All this advice, and all these warnings, both from Joe and now from you, is enough to make a man a nervous wreck!"

"Nonsense, you thrive on all this nervous energy! You have survived this far on that, plus your meticulous safety procedures." Then, pausing for a second, and smiling, continued, "And riding your luck of course!" Another pause, then, "...a very slippery individual!

"You are not very good at being idle. You become like a grumpy old man, but you will have to be a grumpy old man for some time now, because it will be very dangerous, and foolhardy, for you to venture out of here."

"Thank you for that! I presume that you have restored the tunnel entrance? I might need it if I am going to be idle in the barn."

"Yes." she said, "I came in from the rear of the barn and untied the entrance. Your cocktail glasses are safe, still in there."

I went off and resumed my rest in the straw, and Olive went back to her papers.

CHAPTER 19

After a restless few days, Olive informed me that she had to go out with the group and that I was to stay in the barn. The situation had become quite volatile and although I was, to say the least, somewhat grumpy, I had adapted to the situation. There was no other course. I was, therefore, thoroughly delighted when, during the late afternoon, two 'Frenchies' arrived in the barn in a hurry.

"Anglais, Anglais! Olive has sent us; you must leave the barn. It has become dangerous to stay here. You are to come with us to a safe house now. Quickly, we have no time to lose."

I went with them immediately, waving my hand to a few 'Frenchies' in the barn. We got into a well-worn ex-army runabout; a small vehicle with a tailgate and canvas roof. They jumped into the cab, and I hopped into the rear but, just as we started to pull away - I was about to conceal myself under the canvas - I saw 'Onion Face' at the barn. I waved to him and received a very odd response. He drew a pistol and pointed it in the air. He didn't fire it but waved it about, showing the stop signal with his other hand. I, again, waved goodbye and jokingly threw him a kiss. I thought perhaps he was upset that he could not hug me goodbye. As we sped away, I re-thought his actions. 'Was he just frustrated that he had not been able to bid me farewell, or was it a stop signal, not to go?' I paused for thought. There wasn't anything to analyse!

We drove out into the country, following the river. We turned closer, passing a narrow wooden pedestrian bridge, on the left hand side, arriving at a small, rundown cottage alongside the river.

The two Frenchies jumped out smiling, "You will be much safer here Anglais." They seemed much more relaxed now that we had arrived at the cottage.

The three of us entered the cottage. Casting my eye over the interior, I realised there was no rear door. There was a small wooden staircase on the left hand side. Looking towards the rear of the building, the upstairs level only covered three quarters of the room, similar to a large shelf so, glancing upwards, one could see the roof structure. There was a small window at the top of the stairs, which opened outwards, above the narrow towpath and the river. Inside, there was scant furniture; just a small wooden table and two basic wooden chairs.

One of the 'Frenchies', who spoke quite good English assured me, "Don't worry Anglais, it is only very temporary. It's just to keep you safe. Someone will be coming shortly with food and drink. We have to return quickly; the truck must not be seen here. Bonsoir monsieur!"

I wasn't happy. I noticed that they had both got holster bulges. I thought of my own automatic, which I had left with Joe. They seemed very cheerful as they left in the truck.

Yes, as I have just said, I was far from happy. I thought of Olive's warning and 'Onion Face's' antics, but 'if the 'Frenchies' were my enemy, they surely could have dealt with me here and now. Perhaps I am being too critical and suspicious? It could well be safe out here. Obviously, no one appears to have visited for some time and, as the 'Frenchies' said, it will only be for a very short time.'

'No! No! No!' It wasn't right. I felt it wasn't. My instinct told me it wasn't! Olive and I should have had a message password. It was decision time. 'What possible escape plan can I conjure up from this mess?'

Surveying the interior, I noted a small window, covered in dust and cobwebs, on the right hand side of the door. The door had a bolt, and a handle in a rusty unit, but no key. I could see through the muck of the window, down the pathway that we had used, and the small wooden bridge across the river.

I climbed the open wooden staircase. The window at the top of the staircase was a small casement type, which looked as though it was a recent addition to the building; the window opened quite freely, and the timber appeared newly painted. Maybe I was becoming quite paranoid, but I decided to try and make an escape route if possible.

There was no rear door. The only way out would be through the casement window on to the towpath, or into the river. Ghastly, but I could think of no alternative. I put my head out of the window and looked to my right along the towpath, in the opposite direction of the bridge. Further along the river, by the path, were green plants, and reeds or bushes growing in the water.

If the worst should happen and I needed to escape, I would try and pitch into the river, avoiding the towpath. To land on the hard path, I might easily damage my ankle and immobilise myself. Even if I escaped injury, it would be noisy and I would present a target, running away along the path. I would have to: Squeeze through the small window; sit on the narrow sill - being careful of the metal spike, which engages the window stay - then propel myself forward, using my hands and feet, against the wall, so that I would miss the path and land into the river. 'Shoes? I can't swim in shoes. How deep is the river?' I decided that I would relax my laces, so that I would be able to release my shoes easily, if I needed to swim under the surface, beyond the green growth. (When I was younger, I used to swim twenty-two lengths of the swimming baths, which equalled one mile. I also swam the whole of one length under water. This, I did, almost every lunchtime, for quite a period of time.)

If I managed to emerge on the other side of the greenery, it would provide cover, and still be on the near side of the river.

Reasoning, I assumed that my hunters would expect me to swim across to the other side of the river. I was hoping that would be the case. It would mean they would have to run back and cross the wooden bridge. By that time, I could be out of the river and hopefully escape.

'Would I still have shoes?' I would need them! I was working out procedures, and noticed that it was now quite late in the day; the light was fading fast. I did not wish to look for oil lamps, I would prefer to wait in the dark. I felt better now that I had devised an escape plan, but guessed now that maybe I wouldn't need one. I relaxed, but still kept my eye on the approach path, by glancing through the small grubby window by the door.

Suddenly, I saw movement across the river bridge. 'Good! What will be on the menu tonight?' Realising that it was almost the end of the day. There was a group of people. I could not discern them. They crossed over the bridge and started coming down the path towards me. 'Oh my God!' I recognised them. Four, armed German soldiers, holding their rifles with both hands across their chest, accompanied by a civilian. It was a dreadful shock. Another heart pounding experience!

As I have mentioned before, I don't panic, but I moved quickly! I put the chair top under the handle of the door to jam it; slid the bolt across; then moved swiftly up the staircase, to the window. I really had not thought I would have to engage the escape plan. It really was a desperate one. I had to get the timing right. My shoes were already prepped. I was ready to move. My coat was buttoned up; nothing to get caught up on. I was very fit and lean and could quite easily put my knees under my chin. I sat with the end of one cheek of my bottom resting on the small spike. I was ready and focused. I waited. I could hear them approaching the cottage.

There was a hammer blow on the cottage door. That was my signal. I moved, just as I had rehearsed it in my mind. I jettisoned myself, using as much force as I could muster, with the palm of my hands and the heels of my feet, against the cottage wall. My right heel caught the edge of the towpath, the same time I hit the water, causing me to almost belly flop. Pain shot right up my calf. It was not how I had intended to land, but I was able to ground my feet to the bottom of the river. It wasn't as deep as I thought it would be.

Keeping slumped, and under the surface, I breast stroked my way forward, forcing my feet forward at the same time. I felt like a cumbersome hippo! My clothes were dreadfully heavy, as I struggled and strained forward. It was summer, yet the water felt absolutely freezing. An overwhelming feeling encompassed me that I was about to receive a bullet, or bullets, in my back, yet I managed to stay under water until my lungs could hardly cope anymore. Rough weeds and grass brushed my face. This spurred me on, until I was right on my limit without air. I came up inside the weeds, not at the far end as I had planned.

Coming up into darkness, I could hear the soldiers' boots on the wooden bridge. 'Great!' That spurred me on, knowing that they were on the other side of the river. I clutched at the reeds and towpath edge but couldn't get out. I felt as though I weighed a ton. My clothes were full of water and holding me back. I was quite frightened. I had not planned for this.

After many attempts - resulting in bleeding nails and fingers - I did, eventually, manage to get out. I forced myself on my belly to go over the path, into the grass. Trembling with cold, I retrieved my glasses from my coat pocket and put them on. Yes, it was unbelievably cold. It was painful!

Crawling forward, I distanced myself from the river. Although feeling dreadful, I was pleased that I had accomplished what I had planned. 'What next?'

After a long crawl in the dark, I sat up. I tried to get up onto my haunches, but the pain in my heel stopped me. I could not put any weight on it. I felt so heavy, which made it worse. What was my next plan? I could not see anything resembling buildings. 'What's that? Shadowy figures?' I dropped to the ground, staying motionless.

Suddenly, I was grasped under both arms and almost lifted off the ground. I was shocked. Failure, after all that effort! 'My luck has run out. So be it.' I was utterly dejected. I was convinced now that my future was going to be dreadful and short lived.

'No one will know what happened to me, except those who will not tell. I will most probably be lost at sea, or just missing; being technically in the Fleet Air Arm, there wouldn't be a scrap of truth. There couldn't be could there? No one would divulge what was going on' Then a change of thought, 'how long would I have lasted, before the utter wet and freezing cold had taken its toll?' I couldn't walk!

I was carried upright to a waiting car. I wasn't bundled into the back seat. I was carefully lifted into it, with much attention given to my poorly leg. I supposed soldiers, garrison soldiers, being very considerate. The rough stuff will come later with the 'Gestapo'.

Once in the car, I recognised Paul's friend Jean, whom I had laughed with on many occasions. He was talking in a low voice to me. 'So Jean! A traitor!' I could not believe it. 'Who would have suspected Jean?'

It wasn't long before we stopped outside another cottage. While still in the car, Jean must have realised what I was thinking. He comforted me, "It is ok now Anglais."

The driver turned to me and agreed with Jean, "Yes, you are now back with the Resistance. 'Onion Face' alerted Olive. We are the first to arrive. Others are on the way to surround the area, but they will not be needed now, unless the soldiers cause any trouble. There was no danger of you being shot at.; they want you alive. We are telling you now Anglais, because we must be 'security quiet' in the cottage." It was all very hush hush.

We entered the oil lit cottage. A buxom, late middle-aged, woman was there. She left the room. Both the 'Frenchies' helped me to discard my clothes, then rubbed me down vigorously! The buxom woman came back into the room with another towel and clothes. I dressed into an old brown suit which, to say the least, was somewhat roomy! For security reasons, as was said previously, no one spoke a word. The woman gave me a friendly, warm, smile as she treated me to, what I think was, a garlic sausage in pastry.

A mumbling sound, coming from the 'Frenchies', resulted in the woman pouring a glass of cognac and insisting she gave it to me herself. I drank it, as the 'Frenchies' gestured to me, all at once. I sat on a chair, whilst my sodden clothes were picked up. They dried the floor with towels, which they kept together with my clothes; leaving no trace of my presence in the cottage, to safeguard the lady occupant. We swiftly left the cottage. I found that I could walk, limping, without my right heel touching the ground. I felt much better without the weight of my wet clothes. The light bite and cognac had helped me and given me a real boost. However, the clothes, an old brown suit I was wearing, felt very loose and baggy.

We didn't go very far in the car. I was told it wouldn't be safe to go any further. One 'Frenchie' and I alighted from the car, which was then driven away.

It was quite a light sky, with the moon drifting in and out of the clouds.

We walked up the track to a cottage, where the 'Frenchie' opened the door of an outhouse. Inside, there were three bikes. We checked them over and selected one each. I found that I could use the pedal with my right leg, providing I used the front of my foot, which I always did.

We cycled down the pathway, for a few miles, until we came to another dwelling, where we were challenged before entering. There were a large group of armed 'Frenchies' enjoying tasty, hot coffee. I entertained them with my 'special French', before I became a member of the group cycling to a village. There, we met a few gendarmes. It was there I left the group, in the company of one 'Frenchie', who spoke English exceptionally well.

We travelled, to a house, just as dawn was breaking. It was quite well furnished, in comparison to what I had been used to. There was a proper bathroom, which I promptly took advantage of! As I was drying myself, I was surprised to see bruises on my ribs and my arms; they were probably due to my river experience, despite the fact I was wearing clothes. My fingers were painful when gripping and stretching them. Sometimes they locked, but at least my nails had stopped bleeding. I was also beginning to feel more like my real self once again. I realised what a trauma it had been.

I joined the 'Frenchie' for breakfast; served by a nice looking French girl who, I would guess, was not much older than me. The 'Frenchie' wished me to call him Donald. I thought this to be very amusing, every time I addressed him as 'Donald'. He just didn't look like a Donald.

During breakfast, Donald told me, "You will hopefully be airlifted in the near future. You will not move out of here until we get the order to do so."

I got the feeling this was a staging post, and was a routine which had been carried out before.

A few days passed before I was reunited with my own clothes. Now lovely and clean; they had even been pressed.

They were ok, and fitted reasonably well, but the jacket felt tired and floppy, as though it needed a rest on my shoulders.

"You may be leaving for the departure site tomorrow night, depending on the night sky." Donald informed me, later that day.

I felt very odd on hearing that I was leaving. Part of me was glad, another part asked 'How will you cope with no adrenalin loss? No split-second brain decisions? No anticipation and excitement? No dangerous moments? No 'Frenchies' and no Olive?' I wouldn't be allowed to stay, even if I wanted to. My presence wasn't required any more.

The next day, I was very surprised when Donald came into the room with another 'Frenchie', who I recognised immediately; though I can't recall his name. Donald looked on a little perplexed when the smiling 'Frenchie' gave me a cardboard box. I knew instantly what it was.

"Olive wishes you a 'bon voyage!" adding, "She insisted, you must not forget and leave it on the plane!"

Wonderful! Olive! Bless her. My wine glasses. What a lovely parting gift.

I would miss the camaraderie. Emotion welled up inside of me. I wished I wasn't leaving. I spoke to Donald about my friends Paul and 'Onion Face' etc. "Yes," he said, "they are a good group, and are much more aggressive now, since the invasion began. Henri has been killed, and a couple more of them." Although not recalling their names, I must have known them. I was so sad that Henri, so fiery and demonstrative, had gone.

That night, or I should say early the next morning, approximately 01:30, we moved out, walked through the field, and arrived at the departure point.

Eventually, we heard 'Lizzy'. The dim lights on the ground showed, I think they were hand held torches. 'Lizzy' came in and, after a very short run, stopped nearby. The sacks of merchandise were quickly unloaded. I had a quick French embrace from Donald, with whispered wishes. Two boxes were loaded and stacked into the starboard side, then I was on the ladder and into my seat on the port side. We left immediately. I could feel my heart thumping; I was going home!

It was a nervy flight. I would not be happy until we touched down in England. The usual thoughts came back. 'What if the single engine failed? No, it won't! We won't be shot at under the radar, especially going the other way.' I thought of my mother, who didn't like sitting on a train with her back to the engine, when going on holiday to the seaside. I bet she would not have been happy in my position; with my back to the engine, the large fuel tank between us and my back resting on it!

As we approached our landing site, I looked through the portside to see a few odd, pale glimmer of lights coming from the direction of Chichester and wondered if they were farmers in their milking sheds, showing a dim light through partly open doors.

With that passing of thought, we landed. I was home; back into my beloved England.

The End

EPILOGUE

To enlighten you as to what happened to Olive; I met her years later at the Lyons Corner House in London. It was a contrived meeting by Olive, whose correct name was Marguerite. Her mother, who had worked in a foreign embassy during the war (no doubt collecting information) married a diplomat and settled in Sussex, and Olive - who was accompanied by Marie from the café - was returning from a visit with her.

I had recently been accepted into her Majesty's Colonial Service and was on route to London Airport, bound for East Africa, with the East African High Commission.

It was, as you most probably guess, a great hug full reunion. We talked, mostly reminiscing, including amusing incidents regarding my atrocious French. I expected that aspect would be on the conversational menu and I was not disappointed. The amusing theme continued as we were serenaded by a Gypsy Violin Trio at the table, before the three of us, with fond farewells, went our separate ways at London Airport.

Yes, I was on my way to East Africa to another, yet different, kind of mayhem, but that is another story: "Mayhem in Africa", by yours truly.